$3

1 exhaustive and self-contained account
e hydrostatic theory of self-gravitating
stial bodies such as the earth, other plane
d the stars. This theory fully respects t
fects of compressibility, and it should
plicable to configurations of any intern
ucture as it takes rigorous account of
ects produced by rotational or tidal dist
n up to quantities of the order of the squar
the superficial distortion. In the case of t
rth, for instance, the distortion due to t
ntrifugal force flattens the globe so that
lar semi-axis is 21 km. shorter than the equ
rial one. The theory here presented shou
ike possible the prediction of the free for
the terrestrial surface anywhere with
ror margin of less than one yard. It shou
so make possible an evaluation of momer
inertia with comparable accuracy.

This extension of Clairaut's theory repr
nts a significant advance, possibly the mo
nificant advance since Laplace. The need
tend this theory has recently been giv
eat impetus by the advent of artificial sat
es. A detailed knowledge of the properti
the earth's field is indispensable if the orb
such satellites are to be predicted for lo
riods or if atmospheric densities are to l
lculated from observed motions. The theo
also applicable, though with proportionate
s accuracy, to more rapidly rotating maj
nets and close binary stellar systems.

The book is self-contained. Chapter II giv
brief account of the first-order theory nece
y for an understanding of subsequent d
opments and is based on the work of Clai
t, Legendre, and Laplace. It also discuss
airaut's equation along the lines of mo
ent work by Liapounoff and Kopal. Th
ence of the book is found in Chapters I

continued on back fla

continued from front flap

and IV, Chapter III being devoted to the second-order effects of the rotation and of the tides, while Chapter IV deals with the interaction of these effects. The final chapter contains a discussion of the free and forced oscillations of fluid bodies with special regard to the possibility of resonance between them.

Zdeněk Kopal, who is Professor and Head of the Department of Astronomy, University of Manchester, England, and is also a member of the Mathematics Research Center, United States Army, is the author of *Introduction to the Study of Eclipsing Variables, Tables of Supersonic Air Flow Around Cones, Computation of the Elements of Eclipsing Binary Systems, Numerical Analysis, Astronomical Optics,* and *Close Binary Systems,* as well as more than 140 technical papers which have been published in various scientific periodicals. *Figures of Equilibrium of Celestial Bodies* constitutes the results of eight years of investigation and was completed in 1958 while Mr. Kopal worked as guest investigator at the Mathematics Research Center, United States Army, University of Wisconsin.

ZDENĚK KOPAL

PUBLICATION NUMBER 3

of the

MATHEMATICS RESEARCH CENTER

United States Army

The University of Wisconsin

FIGURES OF EQUILIBRIUM OF CELESTIAL BODIES

With Emphasis on Problems of Motion of Artificial Satellites

Zdeněk Kopal

The University of Wisconsin Press

MADISON - 1960

Published by
THE UNIVERSITY OF WISCONSIN PRESS
430 Sterling Court, Madison 6, Wisconsin

Prepared for the camera by Phyllis J. Kern
Printed in the United States of America by the
George Banta Company, Inc., Menasha, Wisconsin

Library of Congress Catalog Card Number 60-60005

CONTENTS

Figures of Equilibrium of Celestial Bodies

I

INTRODUCTION

The beginning of the long history of our subject--namely, the investigation of the figures of equilibrium of self-gravitating compressible fluids, and of the attraction exerted by them at any external point --can be dated with relative precision, for it goes back to the publication, by Alexis Claude Clairaut, of a little treatise entitled La Théorie de la Figure de la Terre, tirée des Principes de l'Hydrostatique, which appeared in Paris in 1743.

Its author was a remarkable personality and a worthy confrère of other great mathematicians in that "century of genius". Born in Paris on May 7, 1713, Clairaut presented his first paper to the French Academy at the age of thirteen. At sixteen, he completed his "Recherches sur le courbe à double courbure", and was elected member of the Academy at eighteen. His Théorie de la Figure de la Terre--a work which, according to Ernst Mach*, inaugurated the rise of mathematical hydrostatics as a scientific discipline--did not appear until Clairaut reached the relatively advanced age of thirty; though he is known to have harbored the essential ideas of his method already on his election to the Academy twelve years previously.

Clairaut's death in 1765 brought to a premature end the career of one of the remarkable mathematicians of the 18th century, and the further development of our subject passed on to the savants of subsequent generations--among whom the contributions due to Legendre and Laplace should in particular be mentioned. As was evident from the title of Clairaut's treatise, the applications of the new theory at that time were primarily geophysical (or planetary); and with the publication of the fifth volume of Laplace's Mécanique Céleste (Paris 1825), the development of the principal features of first-order theory of distortion of self-gravitating compressible fluids (i.e., one regarding the amount of distortion to be sufficiently small for its squares and higher powers to be negligible) was essentially complete. In later decades

*E. Mach, Die Mechanik in ihrer Entwickelung historisch-kritisch dargestellt, Leipzig 1901, pp. 428-434.

of the 19th century, Callandreau and Darwin attempted to extend Clairaut's theory to the terms of second order; but as the applications then in mind were still primarily geophysical (and the departures of the Earth from spheroidal form, due to the second-order rotational terms, are only of the order of ten meters), the elaboration of a consistent second-order theory did not attract many investigators.

The advent of such a theory did not, in fact, become imminent until our own time, when the need of it sprung out of two independent problems: namely, the interpretation of the proximity phenomena in close binary systems, and of the motion of the Earth's artificial satellites. The bearing of Clairaut's theory on certain problems of double-star astronomy was first indicated by Russell (1928) and followed up later by Kopal (1938), Sterne (1939) and others. The interaction between components of close binary systems can give rise to much greater distortion that that suffered by any planet of our solar system, and its consequences are observationally much more significant; besides, the principal distortion in binary stars is caused, not by rotation, but by tides.

Lastly, the dramatic emergence, since 1957, of a whole family of artificial satellites around the Earth has made it indispensable to refine our knowledge of the Earth's gravitational potential to at least the second-order terms, if the observed motions of such satellites are to be correctly computed, and if their interpretation is to yield genuine information on the form and internal structure of the Earth, or on the atmospheric resistance high above its surface. It is primarily in this connection that the second-order effects of the Earth's rotational distortion become observationally significant and require explicit formulation.

The aim of this monograph will be to provide, therefore, a coherent account of the present state of Clairaut's theory of the equilibrium of distorted self-gravitating fluids, complete up to and including the terms of second order. Following these introductory notes, Chapter II will be found to contain a brief account of the first-order theory, necessary for the understanding of subsequent developments and based essentially on the early work of Clairaut, Legendre and Laplace, together with an extensive discussion of the mathematical properties of Clairaut's equation, based largely on the more recent work by Liapounoff and the present writer.

The real gist of the book is contained in the subsequent Chapters III and IV which are concerned with a self-contained exposition of second-order theory: Chapter III being devoted to the second-order effects of the rotation or tides, while Chapter IV deals with the interaction between rotation and tides. The last Chapter V contains a discussion of the free and forced oscillations of fluid bodies, with special regard to the possibility of resonance between them, and the volume is concluded by Bibliographical Notes containing references and historical comments on previous work in this field.

A large part of the subject matter of this book--in particular, all of Chapters III and IV--constitute the results of the author's investigations in this field carried out in the past eight years, which have so far not been published. The work was originally stimulated by certain requirements of double-star astronomy, and completed under the impact of new problems arising from the motions of artificial satellites. This took place mainly during the year 1958, when the writer, on leave from the University of Manchester, worked as a guest investigator at the Mathematics Research Center, United States Army, University of Wisconsin. May he use this opportunity to express his appreciation of the hospitality extended to him by this institution and by its director, Professor R. E. Langer, without whose encouragement the present volume would have scarcely been completed.

II

FIRST-ORDER THEORY

As the title of this book suggests, our principal aim will be to investigate mathematically the figures of equilibrium of self-gravitating compressible fluids, and to specify the external form or gravitational potential of a fluid mass, initially spherical, subject to a given disturbing force. This problem can, in turn, be approached in alternative ways. We can, for instance, depart from the well-known equations of motion of compressible fluids, and attempt to solve them by perturbation methods or otherwise—for the density or pressure; the external boundary can then be defined as a surface over which the pressure and density are zero. This approach has been followed by several investigators; its advantage is the generality with which the disturbing forces reveal their effect on all dependent variables simultaneously; but its disadvantage is the difficulty in obtaining any such solution in a sufficiently explicit form.

There exists, however, an alternative and historically older approach to the problem initiated by Clairaut in the first half of the eighteenth century, which obviates many of these difficulties. In Clairaut's method, the pressure in our fluid makes no appearance in the basic equations, and the density can be an arbitrary (or even discontinuous) function of the radius. The mathematical attack is, instead, concentrated on the construction of explicit expressions for the potential of our configuration—just as the disturbing force is represented solely by its potential —and once this has been found, the complete solution in all its aspects should fall in our laps like a ripe apple. For the external boundary of an equilibrium configuration is defined as an equipotential; and the density (or pressure) distribution inside a distorted configuration can be solved from the Poisson's equation as a Laplacian of the same potential. On account of its simplicity and elegance, as well as its vested historical rights, this will be the method of approach to our problem adopted as a basis in this book.

II-1. THE POTENTIAL; CLAIRAUT'S EQUATION

In order to establish the form and potential energy of a deformable body, in hydrostatic equilibrium of arbitrary internal structure subject to arbitrary distortion, consider a configuration whose density at any point be ρ , and the pressure P . The partial differential equations of its hydrostatic equilibrium are together equivalent to a single total differential equation

$$dP = \rho\, d\Psi \qquad (1-1)$$

where Ψ stands for the complete potential (self-gravitational plus disturbing) of forces acting upon our body. From (1-1) it follows that P is a function of Ψ , and that ρ is either constant, or another function of Ψ . In other words, over any surface of our body characterized by equal density and equal pressure,

$$\Psi = \text{constant} . \qquad (1-2)$$

This contains, in nuce, the complete specification of our problem. In what follows our task will merely be to spell out the explicit form of this equation for any given type of disturbing force.

In order to do so, let us fix our attention to an arbitrary point $M(r, \theta, \phi)$ in the interior of our body (see Figure 1-1) acted upon by the attraction of a stratum comprised between the radii $r = r_0$ and r_1, and let $M'(r', \theta', \phi')$ be an arbitrary point of this stratum. If so, the interior potential U at M will evidently be given by the equation

$$U = G \int \frac{dm'}{\Delta} , \qquad (1-3)$$

where the mass element

$$dm' = \rho r'^2 dr' \sin\theta' d\theta' d\phi' ; \qquad (1-4)$$

while

$$\Delta^2 = r^2 + r'^2 - 2rr'\cos\gamma , \qquad (1-5)$$

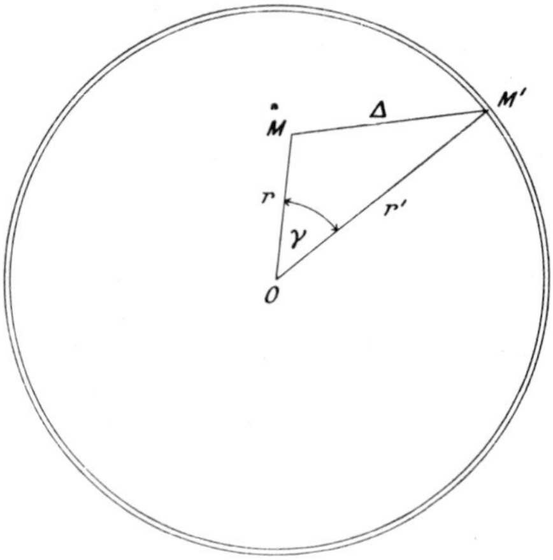

Figure 1-1

where

$$\cos\gamma = \cos\theta\cos\theta' + \sin\theta\sin\theta'\cos(\phi-\phi') \quad . \qquad (1-6)$$

If, moreover, we expand Δ^{-1} in terms of Legendre polynomials $P_n(\cos\gamma)$, equation (1-3) may be rewritten as

$$U = \sum_{n=0}^{\infty} r^n U_n \quad , \qquad (1-7)$$

where

$$U_n = G\int_{r_0}^{r_1}\int_0^{\pi}\int_0^{2\pi} \rho\, r'^{1-n} P_n(\cos\gamma) dr' \sin\theta' d\theta' d\phi' \quad . \qquad (1-8)$$

Let, in the foregoing expressions

$$r' \equiv r(a, \theta', \phi') \qquad (1-9)$$

denote symbolically the equation of an equipotential surface of constant density and pressure. By virtue of the uniqueness of the potential function, only one equipotential surface can pass through any point (i.e., for any value of a); and since the density must, by definition, remain constant over such a surface, it follows that ρ can hereafter be regarded as a function of a single variable a, introduced by the above equation (1-9), and denoting the mean radius of the corresponding equipotential; it is bounded so that $0 < a < a_1$, where a_1 represents the(smallest) root of the equation $\rho(a_1) = 0$. The fact that ρ can thus be regarded as the function of a single variable a suggests that it should be of advantage to change over from r' to a as the new variable of integration on the right-hand side of (1-8); and since,during an integration with respect to r', θ and ϕ' can be regarded as constants, it follows that a transformation from r' to a can be effected by means of the equation

$$dr' = \frac{\partial r'}{\partial a} da \quad . \qquad (1-10)$$

If so, then evidently

$$\int_{r'_0}^{r'_1} \rho(r')^{1-n} dr' = \frac{1}{2-n}\int_{a_0}^{a_1} \rho \frac{\partial}{\partial a}\{(r')^{2-n}\} da \qquad (1-11)$$

for $n \gtrless 2$, and

$$\int_{r'_0}^{r'_1} \rho(r')^{-1} dr' = \int_{a_0}^{a_1} \rho \frac{\partial}{\partial a}(\log r') da \qquad (1-12)$$

for $n = 2$. The individual terms U_n in the expansion (1-7) for the interior potential U assume then the more explicit form

$$U_n = \frac{G}{2-n}\int_{a_0}^{a_1} \rho \frac{\partial}{\partial a}\left\{\int_0^{\pi}\int_0^{2\pi} (r')^{2-n} P_n(\cos\gamma)\sin\theta' d\theta' d\phi'\right\} da \qquad (1-13)$$

for $n \gtrless 2$, and

$$U_2 = G\int^{a_1} \rho\frac{\partial}{\partial a}\left\{\int_0^{\pi}\int_0^{2\pi}(\log r')P_2(\cos\gamma)\sin\theta' d\theta' d\phi'\right\} da , \qquad (1-14)$$

respectively.

In order to progress further, let us assume that the radius-vector r' of an equipotential surface can be expanded in a series of the form

$$r' = a\{1 + \sum_{i,j} Y_j^i(a, \theta', \phi')\} , \qquad (1-15)$$

where the Y's stand for the tesseral harmonic function of their respective parameters*. Let us, moreover, simplify our problem to a first approximation by assuming that the distortion of our configuration is small enough for the squares and cross-products of the individual Y's to be negligible. If so, and if advantage is taken of the fact that the tesseral harmonics Y_j^i are known to satisfy the orthogonality condition

$$\int_0^{\pi}\int_0^{2\pi} P_n(\cos\gamma)Y_j^i(a, \theta', \phi')\sin\theta' d\theta' d\phi' = \frac{4\pi}{2j+1}Y_j^i(a, \theta, \phi) \qquad (1-16)$$

when $j = n$, and zero for $j \neq n$, equation (1-7) may easily be reduced to the form

$$U = U_0 + \sum_{j=1}^{\infty}\frac{4\pi G r^j}{2j+1}\int_{a_0}^{a_1}\rho\frac{\partial}{\partial a}(a^{2-j}Y_j^i)da , \qquad (1-17)$$

where we have abbreviated

$$U_0 = 4\pi G\int_{a_0}^{a_1}\rho a\, da . \qquad (1-18)$$

The exterior potential V at $M(a, \theta, \phi)$ can be found and expressed in terms of a by closely analogous methods. In order to do so, let us start from the definition

$$V = \sum_{n=0}^{\infty} V_n r^{-(n+1)} , \qquad (1-19)$$

---

* The convergence of this expansion has given rise to considerable discussion ever since this series was first introduced by Laplace; and cannot, in fact, be guaranteed to obtain in the most general case. (Cf., e.g., F. Hopfner, Physikalische Geodäsie, Acad. Verlag MBH, 1933; or W. S. Jardetsky, Theories of Figures of Celestial Bodies, New York 1958, pp. 17-19.) We do not wish, however, to discuss its problem in this place because, for the purpose of our investigation, the formal convergence of an infinite series of the form (1-11) is really irrelevant. What matters are the asymptotic properties of its first few terms—for these alone we shall be able to construct by any practicable procedure —and these can be tested a posteriori (cf. sec. III-6) on the limiting homogeneous and centrally-condensed models for which the whole solution is obtainable in a closed form.

where

$$V_n = G\int P_n(\cos\gamma)\, r'^n dm' \; . \tag{1-20}$$

For $n = 0$,

$$V_0 = G\int dm' = G m_0 \; , \tag{1-21}$$

where m_0 denotes the mass of our configuration interior to a_0 . Furthermore, as

$$\int_0^{r'_0} \rho(r')^{j+2} dr' = \frac{1}{j+3}\int_0^{a_0} \rho \frac{\partial}{\partial a}\{(r')^{j+3}\} da \tag{1-22}$$

and, therefore,

$$V_j = \frac{1}{j+3}\int_0^{a_0} \rho \frac{\partial}{\partial a}\left\{\int_0^{\pi}\int_0^{2\pi} (r')^{j+3} P_j(\cos\gamma)\sin\theta' d\theta' d\phi'\right\} da \tag{1-23}$$

for any value of j , on changing over from r' to a by means of (1-10)-(1-15) and making use of (1-23) equation (1-19) can, to the same accuracy, be expressed as

$$V = G\frac{m_0}{r} + \sum_{j=1}^{\infty} \frac{4\pi G}{(2j+1) r^{j+1}} \int_0^{a_0} \rho \frac{\partial}{\partial a}(a^{j+3} Y_j^i) da \; . \tag{1-24}$$

It is, moreover, possible to prove that if the center of our coordinate system coincides with the center of mass of the configuration, the first tesseral harmonic $Y_1(a;\theta,\phi)$ must necessarily vanish. For, if x, y, z denote the coordinates of center of gravity of a body arbitrarily placed, it follows, by definition, that

$$\begin{bmatrix} x \\ y \\ z \end{bmatrix} m_0 = \int_0^{r_0}\int_0^{\pi}\int_0^{2\pi} \rho r'^2 \begin{bmatrix} r'\sin\theta'\cos\phi' \\ r'\sin\theta'\sin\phi' \\ r'\cos\theta' \end{bmatrix} dr' \sin\theta' d\theta' d\phi'$$

$$= \int_0^{a_0} \rho \frac{\partial}{\partial a}\left\{\int_0^{\pi}\int_0^{2\pi} \frac{r'^4}{4} \begin{bmatrix} \sin\theta'\cos\phi' \\ \sin\theta'\sin\phi' \\ \cos\theta' \end{bmatrix} \sin\theta' d\theta' d\phi'\right\} da \tag{1-25}$$

by (1-10). Now the most general expression for a tesseral harmonic of order one is known to be

$$Y_1(a;\theta',\phi') = A\sin\theta'\cos\phi' + B\sin\theta'\sin\phi' + C\cos\theta' \; , \tag{1-26}$$

where A, B, C stand for some functions of a . Let us, therefore, insert (1-26) together with (1-15) in (1-25): the orthogonality of tesseral harmonics will annihilate all terms but Y_1. If, moreover, we multiply each of the three equations (1-25) by A, B, C, respectively, their sum discloses that

$$(x+y+z)m_0 = \int_0^{a_0} \rho \frac{\partial}{\partial a} \left\{ \int_0^{\pi} \int_0^{2\pi} [a^2 Y_1(a;\theta',\phi')]^2 \sin\theta' d\theta' d\phi' \right\} da \quad . \tag{1-27}$$

If, eventually, all three coordinates x, y, z are made to vanish by placing the center of mass of our configuration at the origin, the integral on the right-hand side of equation (1-27) must likewise be equal to zero. But as the integrand in the curly brackets is non-negative, this can be true only if

$$Y_1(a;\theta',\phi') \equiv 0 \tag{1-28}$$

for all values of θ' and ϕ' over the sphere. Hence, by a suitable choice of coordinates the non-vanishing terms in the summations on the right-hand sides of both (1-17) and (1-24) can be made to commence with $j = 2$; and in all that follows it will be assumed that this is actually the case.

The total potential arising from the mass of the distorted configuration is then equal to the sum

$$U + V = U_0 + \frac{V_0}{r} + \sum_{j=2}^{\infty} \frac{4\pi G r^j}{2j+1} \int_a^{a_1} \rho \frac{\partial}{\partial a}(a^{2-j} Y_j^i) da$$
$$+ \sum_{j=2}^{\infty} \frac{4\pi G}{(2j+1) r^{j+1}} \int_0^{a} \rho \frac{\partial}{\partial a}(a^{j+3} Y_j^i) da \quad , \tag{1-29}$$

where we have replaced—there should be no danger of confusion—a_0 in the limits of our integrals by a. Lastly, let us suppose that the disturbing potential V' — whatever its origin — is also expansible in terms of surface harmonics $P_j^i(\theta,\phi)$ in a series of the form

$$V' = \sum_{i,j} c_{i,j} r^j P_j^i(\theta,\phi) \quad , \tag{1-30}$$

where the $c_{i,j}$'s are quantities—as yet unspecified—depending on the nature of distortion. If so, the total potential Ψ of forces acting on any arbitrary point will be represented by the sum

$$\Psi = U + V + V' \quad , \tag{1-31}$$

where U and V are already specified by equations (1-17) and (1-24) and their sum is given by (1-29). Now if, in conformity with (1-2), the function Ψ is to remain constant over any surface of equal pressure or density, over which $r = a\{1 + \sum Y_j^i\}$, the coefficients corresponding to the individual values of j in Ψ must all be equal to zero; and this will be true if, and only if,

$$Y_j^i \int_0^a \rho a^2 da - \frac{1}{(2j+1)a^j} \int_0^a \rho \frac{\partial}{\partial a}(a^{j+3} Y_j^i) da$$

$$- \frac{a^{j+1}}{2j+1} \int_a^{a_1} \rho \frac{\partial}{\partial a}(a^{2-j} Y_j^i) da = \frac{c_{i,j}}{4\pi G} a^{j+1} P_j^i(\theta, \phi) \tag{1-32}$$

for any i, j, correctly to the first order in small quantities. This well-known result is generally referred to in the literature as Clairaut's equation, although its above form (for any j) was not actually derived until by Legendre. And lest any reader be under the impression that only we happen to live in a century of genius, and that all our science dates back to yesterday, let it be stated that the essential part of the theory outlined in this section so far was discovered (though perhaps not in the same form) by Alexis Claude Clairaut, at the age of eighteen, 228 years ago.

Clairaut's equation (1-32) implicitly specifies the tesseral harmonics Y_j^i describing the actual form of the equipotential level surfaces as distorted by an external force deriving from the potential (1-30). As such, it will prove to be of central importance for our problem, and its general properties as well as particular solutions will merit a detailed study. Before we embark upon it in the next section, we wish to invoke first certain elementary transformations furnishing results of direct interest. Thus, in order to deduce a more explicit form of the Y_j^i's at the external boundary of our configuration, let us multiply both sides of equation (1-32) by a^j, differentiate with respect to a *, and divide by a^{2j}: we obtain

$$\left\{\frac{jY_j^i}{a^{j+1}} + \frac{1}{a^j}\frac{\partial Y_j^i}{\partial a}\right\} \int_0^a \rho a^2 da - \int_a^{a_1} \rho \frac{\partial}{\partial a}(a^{2-j} Y_j^i) da$$

$$= \frac{c_{i,j}}{4\pi G}(2j+1) P_j^i(\theta, \phi) . \tag{1-33}$$

*In doing so we tacitly assume the $c_{i,j}$'s to be constants. This need not, however, necessarily always be the case; and modifications arising if some of the c's happen to be functions of a will be considered at a later stage (cf. sec. III-5).

As, at the boundary, $a = a_1$ and

$$4\pi \int_0^{a_1} \rho a^2 \, da = m_1 \tag{1-34}$$

denotes the mass of the distorted configuration as a whole, the second integral on the left-hand side of (1-33) vanishes and the first can be replaced by $m_1/4\pi$.

The remaining part of equation (1-33) can, moreover, be symbolically solved for the surface values of $Y_j^i(a_1)$ in the form

$$Y_j^i(a_1;\theta,\phi) = c_{i,j}\Delta_j \frac{a_1^{j+1}}{Gm_1} P_j^i(\theta,\phi) , \tag{1-35}$$

where we have abbreviated

$$\Delta_j = \frac{2j+1}{j+\eta_j(a_1)} ; \tag{1-36}$$

$\eta_j(a_1)$ denoting the surface value of the logarithmic derivative

$$\eta_j(a) = \frac{a}{Y_j^i}\frac{dY_j^i}{da} . \tag{1-37}$$

The foregoing solution of (1-33) is, therefore, not explicit, as Y_j^i remains involved on the right-hand side of (1-35) through the surface value of its logarithmic derivative (1-37).

In order to investigate more closely the effect of internal structure on the external form of a distorted configuration, let us return to equation (1-33). Differentiating it once more with respect to a we find that

$$a^2 \frac{d^2Y}{da^2} + 6\frac{\rho}{\bar{\rho}}\left(a\frac{dY}{da} + Y\right) = j(j+1)Y , \tag{1-38}$$

where

$$\eta_j(a) = \frac{a}{Y_j^i}\frac{dY_j^i}{da} . \tag{1-39}$$

denotes the mean density interior to a ; and the logarithmic derivative η_j of Y_j^i as given by equation (1-37) will, consequently, be bound to satisfy the nonlinear differential equation

$$a\frac{d\eta_j}{da} + 6\frac{\rho}{\bar{\rho}}(\eta_j + 1) + \eta_j(\eta_j - 1) = j(j+1) , \tag{1-40}$$

which is of first order in the dependent variable.

At the origin $(a = 0$ and $\rho/\bar{\rho} = 1)$, this equation reveals at once that

$$\eta_j(0) = j - 2 \ , \tag{1-41}$$

a condition which is sufficient for a complete specification of the desired solution for any given function $\rho/\overline{\rho}$. A similar specification of the corresponding solutions of the second-order equation (1-38) for Y requires, however, a knowledge of two boundary conditions: and these are distributed between both ends of the interval $(0, a_1)$. At the origin, in conformity with (1-37) and (1-41) we should expect that

$$Y_j(a) \simeq k a^{j-2} \ , \tag{1-42}$$

where k is a characteristic constant to be determined with the aid of the nonhomogeneous condition (1-35) requiring that, at the surface,

$$jY_j(a_1) + a_1\left(\frac{dY_j}{da}\right)_1 = \frac{2j+1}{Gm_1} c_{i,j} a_1^{2j+1} \ . \tag{1-43}$$

Equation (1-38) is usually referred to also as Clairaut's equation (being a simple consequence of 1-32), and (1-40) frequently carries the name of Radau's equation--in honor of another distinguished French astronomer who made extensive use of it in the latter part of the nineteenth century. As usual, however, such simple terminology does but partial justice to historical truth; for Clairaut deduced equation (1-32) rather than (1-38) and only in the particular case of $j = 2$; equation (1-38) as it stands above did not make its appearance until the works of Laplace, and the substitution (1-37) leading to (1-40) had been employed before Radau's time. If we persist, in what follows, to associate names of Clairaut and Radau with the linear second-order equation (1-38) and the nonlinear first-order equation (1-40), the critical reader may regard such terminology at least as convenient labels which may save some confusion.

Before concluding the present section, we are in a position to evaluate more explicitly the integrals on the right-hand sides of the expansions (1-17) and (1-24) for the internal and external potentials of our distorted body. Equation (1-32) specialized for $a = a_1$ reveals at once that

$$\int_0^{a_1} \rho \frac{\partial}{\partial a}(a^{j+3} Y_j^i) da = (2j+1)\, a_1^{2j+1} (\Delta_j - 1) \frac{c_{i,j}}{4\pi G} P_j^i(\theta, \phi), \tag{1-44}$$

by virtue of (1-35). On the other hand, a multiplication of (1-32) by a^j , differentiation with respect to a , and subsequent multiplication by a^{2j} yields

$$\int_a^{a_1} \rho \frac{\partial}{\partial a}(a^{2-j} Y_j^i) da = \frac{Y_j^i}{a^{j+1}} \{j + \eta_j(a)\} \int_0^a \rho a^2 da - \frac{2j+1}{4\pi G} c_{i,j} P_j^i(\theta, \phi) \tag{1-45}$$

Inserting (1-45) in (1-17) we find that, at an arbitrary internal point in our configuration, the potential arising from the mass of a shell comprised between the mean radii a and a_1 assumes the more explicit form

$$U = U_0 + G \sum_{j=2}^{\infty} \left\{ \left[\frac{j + \eta_j(a)}{2j+1} \right] \frac{m(a)}{a} Y_j^i(a;\theta,\phi) - \frac{c_{i,j}\, a^j P_j^i(\theta,\phi)}{G} \right\} , \tag{1-46}$$

where

$$m(a) = 4\pi \int_0^a \rho a^2 \, da \tag{1-47}$$

denotes the mass of the core interior to a . Furthermore, by an insertion of (1-44) in (1-24), the potential arising from the mass of a core interior to a similarly becomes

$$V = \frac{V_0}{a} + G \sum_{j=2}^{\infty} \left\{ \frac{j+1-\eta_j(a)}{2j+1} \right\} \frac{m(a)}{a} Y_j^i(a;\theta,\phi) \tag{1-48}$$

for $r = a$; while for points exterior to our configuration $(r > a_1)$,

$$V(r) = G\frac{m_1}{r} + \sum_{j=2}^{\infty} \frac{a_1^{2j+1}}{r^{j+1}} (\Delta_j - 1)\, c_{i,j}\, P_j^i(\theta,\phi) , \tag{1-49}$$

where we substituted for $Y_j^i(a_1;\theta,\phi)$ from (1-35) and abbreviated $m_1 \equiv m(a_1)$.

The results of the foregoing paragraph should enable us also to predict the <u>variation of gravity</u> over the surface of a distorted configuration. For this should obviously be derivable from the total potential Ψ of forces acting on any surface point, as defined by equation (1-33), which on the surface $(a = a_1)$ reduces to

$$\Psi(a_1) = G\frac{m_1}{r} + \sum_{j=2}^{\infty} c_{i,j} \left\{ (\Delta_j - 1)\frac{a_1^{2j+1}}{r^{j+1}} + r^j \right\} P_j^i(\theta,\phi) \tag{1-50}$$

by use of (1-30) and (1-49). The surface gravity g is then defined by the relation

$$g = -\frac{d}{dn}\Psi(a_1) , \tag{1-51}$$

where d/dn denotes the normal derivative to the surface.

For a distorted configuration this normal makes, in general, an angle with the radius-vector r which is of the order of magnitude of Y_j^i , so that its cosine differs from unity only by quantities of second order, which in this section we propose to ignore. To the first order of such quantities we may, therefore, set

$$g = -\frac{d\Psi(a_1)}{dr} \tag{1-52}$$

to be evaluated at $r = a_1(1 + \Sigma Y)$. Differentiating (1-50) we find that a spherical harmonic distortion Y_j^i produces, on the surface, a variation of gravity as given by the equation

$$\frac{g - g_0}{g_0} = -\{1 + \eta_j(a_1)\}Y_j^i , \tag{1-53}$$

where $g_0 \equiv Gm_1/r^2$; and if a number of distinct Y_j^i 's are superposed,

$$\frac{g - g_0}{g_0} = -\sum_{i,j}\{1 + \eta_j(a_1)\}Y_j^i . \tag{1-54}$$

To each separate harmonic distortion there corresponds a variation of surface gravity such that the fractional variation of this gravity is proportional to the fractional variation of the radius-vector.

II-2. CLAIRAUT'S EQUATION: GENERAL PROPERTIES AND PARTICULAR SOLUTIONS

In the preceding section we have found that the form of equipotential surfaces of a distorted fluid configuration can be uniquely described in terms of the tesseral harmonics $Y_j^i(a;\theta,\phi)$ which satisfy the integral equation (1-32) and whose surface form $(a = a_1)$ is given by equation (1-35). This form, as well as the external potential (1-46) of the distorted body was, moreover, found to depend on its internal structure (i.e., the density function $\rho(a)$) only through the surface value $\eta_j(a_1)$ of the logarithmic derivative of Y_j . In order to establish the values of such derivatives at $a = a_1$ and their dependence on the whole march of the density distribution in the interior, it will be necessary to investigate the behaviour of the functions $Y_j(a)$ or $\eta_j(a)$, not only at $a = a_1$, but throughout the whole range $0 \leq a \leq a_1$. The aim of the present section will be to outline the course of such an analysis for an arbitrary function of $\rho(a)$, as well as to enumerate such cases of $\rho(a)$ for which the Clairaut and Radau's equations become directly integrable.

In order to do so, let us first confine our attention to Radau's first-order equation (1-40).

In considering the behaviour of its solutions in the $a - \eta$ plane, we may note first that (1-40) defines the first derivative $\eta'_j(a)$ in terms of a and η_j everywhere except at the origin. Along the axis $a = 0$ the function $\eta'_j(a)$ ceases to be holomorphic, and (1-40) can be satisfied by η_j assuming the alternative values of $j - 2$ or $-j - 3$. At the points specified by the coordinates $(0, j - 2)$ and $(0, j - 3)$ the integral curves obeying equation (1-40) are thus not determined uniquely. It can, however, be shown* that, of the total manifold of such curves passing through an arbitrary point of the $a - \eta$ plane, only one will pass through $(0, j - 2)$; all others pass through $(0, j - 3)$. Therefore, the initial condition (1-41) is sufficient to ensure the uniqueness of the particular solution of the equation (1-40) which is of interest to us.

In further quest of the general properties of such solutions, let us return to equation (1-32). If we divide it by a^{j+1}, differentiate with respect to a and subsequently multiply by a^{2j+2}, we establish that

$$\int_0^a \rho \frac{\partial}{\partial a}(a^{j+3} Y_j^i)\, da = a^j Y_j^i \{j + 1 - \eta_j(a)\} \int_0^a \rho a^2 da \; , \qquad (2\text{-}1)$$

which on partial integration assumes the form

$$a^j Y_j^i \{[j + 1 - \eta_j(a)] \int_0^a \rho a^2 da - \rho a^3\} = -\int_0^a \frac{d\rho}{da} a^{j+3} Y_j^i da \; . \qquad (2\text{-}2)$$

Making use of (1-39) and of the fact that, by differentiation

$$\rho = \bar{\rho}\{1 + \frac{1}{3}\frac{a}{\rho}\frac{d\bar{\rho}}{da}\} = \bar{\rho}(1 - \frac{1}{3}f) \; , \qquad (2\text{-}3)$$

we readily see from (2-2) that

$$a^{j+3} Y_j^i \{j - 2 + f - \eta_j(a)\}\bar{\rho} = -3\int_0^a \frac{d\rho}{da} a^{j+3} Y_j^i da \; . \qquad (2\text{-}4)$$

Now if the right-hand side of this equation is a positive quantity,** it follows from its left-hand side that

$$\eta_j(a) \leq j - 2 + f \; . \qquad (2\text{-}5)$$

The quantity f as introduced by equation (2-3) is, in turn, constrained to satisfy the inequality

$$0 \leq f \leq 3 \; ; \qquad (2\text{-}6)$$

---

*Cf., H. Poincaré, Leçons sur les Figures d'Equilibre, Paris 1903, pp. 67-81.

**The condition that ρ' be negative for $0 < a < a_1$ is sufficient, though not necessary, for this to be true. The validity of (2-5) would not be impaired by the occurrence of local positive density-gradients as long as these do not alter the sign of the integral on the right-hand side of (2-4).

its left-hand side being necessarily true if $\overline{\rho}'$ in (2-2) is negative; the right-hand side, because ρ is positive. In consequence, any variation of $\eta_j(a)$ that is possible under such conditions will be limited by

$$j - 2 \leq \eta_j(a) \leq j - 2 + f \quad . \tag{2-7}$$

Let us inquire next as to the behaviour of the solutions of Radau's equation (1-40), subject to the initial condition (1-41), in the $\eta - \eta'$ plane. For the limiting model of a homogeneous configuration $f = 0$ and $\rho/\overline{\rho} = 1$, so that (1-40) reduces to the parabola

$$a\eta' = j(j+1) - (\eta+2)(\eta+3) \quad ; \tag{2-8}$$

while for centrally condensed model $(f = 3, \ \rho/\overline{\rho} = 0)$ equation (1-40) reduces likewise to

$$a\eta' = j(j+1) - \eta(\eta-1) \quad . \tag{2-9}$$

On the other hand, for the values of $f = \eta + 2 - j$ at which (2-5) becomes an equality,

$$a\eta' = (j+1)(j+2) - (2j-1)\eta + \eta^2 \quad . \tag{2-10}$$

Any point of the solution of Radau's equation (1-40) for a configuration intermediate in structure between homogeneous and mass-point models must lie, in the $\eta - \eta'$ plane, in the region limited between the foregoing parabolae; in point of fact, for such models as render the integral on the right-hand side of equation (2-4) positive, the permitted region is comprised solely between the parabolae (2-8) and (2-10) intersecting at the points $j - 2$ and $j + 1$. A plot of these limiting curves is diagrammatically shown on the accompanying Figure 2-1; and these delimit an area in which $\eta'_j(a)$ can be both positive and negative.

In order to investigate further the possible behaviour of $\eta_j(a)$ in this area, let us differentiate Radau's equation (1-40) with respect to a to obtain

$$a\eta'' + 2\eta'(\eta+3) = 2(f\eta)' + 2f' \quad . \tag{2-11}$$

If η'' is to vanish anywhere within this area, either both sides of this equation must vanish identically (i.e., η must pass through an inflection point and increase thereafter), or we must have

$$\eta'(\eta+3) = (f\eta)' + f' \quad . \tag{2-12}$$

This latter equation can be readily integrated as it stands, and its particular solution satisfying the initial condition $\eta_j(0) = j - 2$ assumes

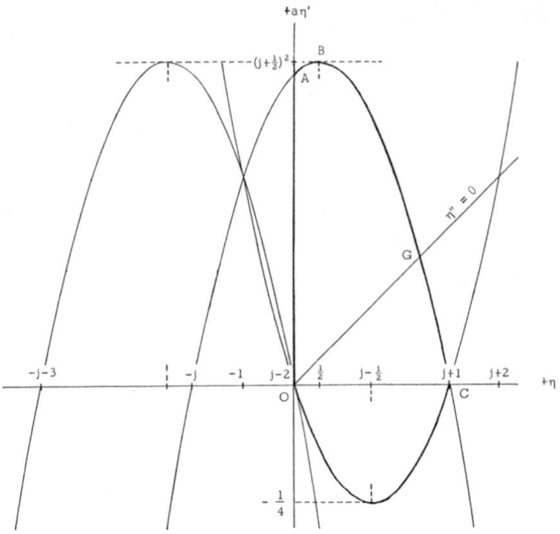

Figure 2-1

the form

$$2(\eta+1)f = \eta(\eta+6) - (j-2)(j+4) , \tag{2-13}$$

which inserted in (1-40) yields

$$a\,\eta' = \eta - j + 2 . \tag{2-14}$$

Therefore, the locus $\eta'' = 0$ of inflection points will be represented on Figure 2-1 by a straight line, passing through the point $\eta = j - 2$, and inclined by 45° to the locus $\eta' = 0$ of the extrema which coincides with the η-axis.

At the centre of our configuration $\eta_j(0) = j - 2$, and in its immediate neighbourhood $\eta'(a) > 0$. Therefore, $\eta_j(a)$ will at first be an increasing function of a ; but its subsequent behaviour may differ in different parts of the diagram. Thus in the domain OABG of Figure 2-1 we have $\eta'' > 0$, η' positive and increasing, and thus η increasing throughout. In the domain OGC $\eta'' < 0$ and η' is therefore diminishing but still positive, so that η increases at a diminishing rate. Lastly, in the region OCD we find that both η'' and η' are negative and, therefore, η will be diminishing throughout. The general trend of variation of $\eta_j(a)$ in the interior of our configuration can, therefore, be clearly specified by the surface values of $\eta_j(a_1)$ and $\eta'_j(a_1)$ alone. If $\eta'_j(a_1) > 0$, $\eta_j(a)$ will be an increasing function throughout the interior, or a decreasing function if $\eta'_j(a_1) < 0$. Since, moreover, the line $\eta'' = 0$ lies above that of $\eta' = 0$ between $j - 2 < \eta < j + 1$, it is obvious that $\eta_j(a)$ can never have a minimum in the interior. Therefore, if $\eta_j(a)$ is an increasing function at the surface of our configuration, it will remain so throughout its mass; but if it is diminishing at the surface, it will possess a maximum in the interior.

The fact that the line $\eta'' = 0$ lies above that of $\eta' = 0$ for $\eta > j - 2$ in the $\eta - \eta'$ coordinates (see again Figure 2-1) entails one specific consequence restricting possible density distribution of our configurations. In order to demonstrate it, let us return to equation (2-11) and solve it for $\eta''_j(a)$ at a point when $\eta'_j(a) = 0$: we find that, at that point,

$$\eta'' = 2(\eta + 1)f' \quad . \tag{2-15}$$

Now the fact that the function $\eta''_j(a)$ cannot have a minimum for $0 < a < a_1$ reveals that f' must remain positive throughout that domain — i.e., that

$$\frac{d}{da}\left(\frac{\rho}{\bar{\rho}}\right) \leq 0 \tag{2-16}$$

or, in more specific terms, that

$$3\rho\bar{\rho} \leq 3\rho^2 - \bar{\rho}(a\rho') \quad . \tag{2-17}$$

The equality sign holds good when $\rho = \bar{\rho}$ = constant, and corresponds to $f' = 0$ leading to an inflection point $\eta'' = \eta' = 0$ at $\eta = j - 2$. We know, in fact, that the solution of Radau's equation (1-40) for the homogeneous model (ρ = constant) reduces indeed to the point $\eta_j(a) = j - 2$ in the $\eta - \eta'$ plane. The conditions

$$\rho' < 0 \quad \text{and} \quad \rho'' < 0 \quad , \tag{2-18}$$

or

$$\bar{\rho}' < 0 \quad \text{and} \quad \bar{\rho}'' < 0 \quad , \tag{2-19}$$

are sufficient, but not necessary, for the inequalities (2-18) and (2-19) to hold good.

For certain specific density distributions $\rho(a)$ the requisite solutions of Clairaut's or Radau's equations can be constructed in a closed form. Thus, if our configuration were homogeneous (i.e., if $\rho = \bar{\rho}$ for any value of a), equation (1-38) assumes the form

$$a^2\frac{d^2Y_j}{da^2} + 6a\frac{dY_j}{da} + (3+j)(2-j)Y_j = 0 \quad . \tag{2-20}$$

The roots of its indicial equation being $j - 2$ and $-(j + 3)$, the particular solution which is non-singular at the origin clearly becomes

$$Y_j(a) = k a^{j-2} \quad , \tag{2-21}$$

where k is a constant; and, by (1-37)

$$\eta_j(a) = j - 2 . \tag{2-22}$$

If, on the other hand, the whole mass of our configuration were condensed at its center, surrounded by a tenuous atmosphere whose mass can be ignored (i.e., if $\rho/\bar{\rho} = \infty$ for $a = 0$ and zero for $a > 0$)

$$a^2 \frac{d^2 Y_j}{da^2} - j(j+1)Y_j = 0 , \tag{2-23}$$

which is satisfied by

$$Y_j(a) = ka^{j+1} , \tag{2-24}$$

leading to

$$\eta_j(a) = j + 1 . \tag{2-25}$$

Lastly, if the whole mass of our configuration were confined to an infinitesimally thin surface shell (so that $\rho/\rho_m = 0$ for $a < a_1$; and ∞ at $a = a_1$) the solution of equations (1-38) or (1-40) reduces to

$$\left.\begin{aligned} Y_j(a_1) &= ka^{-1} , \\ \eta_j(a_1) &= -1 . \end{aligned}\right\} \tag{2-26}$$

Thus, if we presume nothing on the density distribution in the interior of our configuration, the absolute limits of the function $\eta_j(a_1)$ on the surface are

$$-1 \le \eta_j(a_1) \le j + 1 \tag{2-27}$$

and, hence, by (1-36) the constants Δ_j factoring the superficial distortion $Y_j(a_1)$ as given by equation (1-35) are found to be comprised between the limits

$$1 \le \Delta_j \le \frac{2j + 1}{j - 1} \tag{2-28}$$

for $j = 2, 3, 4$. If, moreover, the density is supposed not to increase outwards, the foregoing inequality (2-28) becomes restricted to

$$1 \le \Delta_j \le \frac{2j + 1}{2(j + 1)} . \tag{2-29}$$

It may also be noticed that, whatever the structure,

$$\Delta_j \ge \Delta_{j+1} . \tag{2-30}$$

The inequality (2-29) has first been proved (for $j = 2$) by Clairaut; and that of (2-28) by Kopal. The latter reveals that, in any given field of external force, the superficial distortion of a configuration whose whole mass is confined to an infinitesimally thin surface shell would be twice as large as if the configuration were homogeneous, and five times as large as that appropriate for a mass-point model.

Apart from these limiting cases, Clairaut's or Radau's equations admit of closed solutions also for certain intermediate density distributions in the interior. In order to exhibit them, we find it convenient to change over from Y_j in (1-38) to a new variable y defined by

$$y = \frac{a^3\bar{\rho}}{3} Y_j , \qquad (2\text{-}31)$$

so that

$$\eta_j = \frac{a}{y}\frac{dy}{da} - 3\frac{\rho}{\bar{\rho}} . \qquad (2\text{-}32)$$

In consequence, equation (1-38) will assume the form

$$\frac{d^2y}{da^2} = \left\{\frac{j(j+1)}{a^2} + g(a)\right\} y , \qquad (2\text{-}33)$$

where we have abbreviated

$$g(a) = \frac{3}{a\bar{\rho}}\frac{d\rho}{da} . \qquad (2\text{-}34)$$

Two cases arise immediately in which equation (2-33) becomes solvable in finite terms: namely, if

$$\rho(a) = ka^{-n} , \qquad (2\text{-}35)$$

where both k and $n(<3)$ are suitable constants—so that, in this particular case,

$$g(a) = \frac{n(n-3)}{a^2} ; \qquad (2\text{-}36)$$

or again if the internal density distribution is such that

$$g(a) = -m^2 , \qquad (2\text{-}37)$$

m being an arbitrary constant. The actual density distribution $\rho(a)$ consistent with this latter assumption follows as a solution of the differential equation

$$\frac{1}{a^2}\frac{d}{da}\left(a^2\frac{d\rho}{da}\right) + m^2\rho = 0 , \qquad (2\text{-}38)$$

obtained by differentiation of (2-37) with respect to a; and its particular solution rendering $\rho(0) \equiv \rho_c$ finite is easily found to be

$$\frac{\rho}{\rho_c} = \frac{\sin ma}{ma} \quad . \tag{2-39}$$

If, moreover, we impose the condition that ρ is to vanish at $a_1 = \pi$ (say), it follows that $m = 1$ and, in consequence, $\rho/\rho_c = a^{-1} \sin a$.*

Let us return now to equation (2-33). Inserting (2-36) we find the particular solution of (2-30) vanishing at the origin to assume the form

$$y_j(a) = C_j a^{\frac{1}{2} + \sqrt{(j + \frac{1}{2})^2 + n(n-3)}} , \tag{2-40}$$

where the C_j's are arbitrary constants; and, by (2-32), the corresponding functions $\eta_j(a)$ are given by

$$\eta_j(a) = \sqrt{j + \tfrac{1}{2})^2 + n(n-3)} - \tfrac{5}{2} + n \tag{2-41}$$

for $a > 0$.

If, on the other hand, $g(a)$ is to be given by (2-37), the requisite particular solution of (2-33) can be expressed in terms of the Bessel functions $J_{j+\frac{1}{2}}(a)$ of fractional order in the form

$$y_j(a) = C_j a^{1/2} J_{j+\frac{1}{2}}(a) \quad . \tag{2-42}$$

As is well known, the Bessel functions of half-integral order are expressible in closed form in terms of trigonometric functions: in particular,

$$\left. \begin{aligned} J_{1/2}(a) &= \sqrt{2/\pi a} \; \sin a \; , \\ J_{-1/2}(a) &= \sqrt{2/\pi a} \; \cos a \; ; \end{aligned} \right\} \tag{2-43}$$

and those of higher order can be successively built up by means of the recursion formula

$$J_{n+1}(a) = (2n/a)\, J_n(a) - J_{n-1}(a) \quad . \tag{2-44}$$

In consequence, all functions $y_j(a)$ should be expressible in terms of suitable combinations of $a^{-1} \sin a$ and $a^{-1} \cos a$ factored by polynomials in descending powers of a ; and their logarithmic differentiation reveals that, on the surface $(a_1 = \pi)$,

*It may be noted that the differential equation (2-38) and its solution (2-39) represent nothing but the internal density distribution of a polytropic gas sphere characterized by the polytropic index $n = 1$ — a model which made its first appearance, in this context, in the writings of Laplace almost a century before Emden's work.

$$\left.\begin{aligned} \eta_2(\pi) &= \frac{\pi^2}{3} - 2 , \\ \eta_3(\pi) &= \frac{6\pi^2 - 45}{15 - \pi^2} , \\ \eta_4(\pi) &= \frac{\pi^4 - 55\pi^2 + 420}{10\pi^2 - 105} , \end{aligned}\right\} \qquad (2\text{-}45)$$

etc., leading to

$$\left.\begin{aligned} \Delta_2 &= 1{\cdot}519\ 820 \ \ldots , \\ \Delta_3 &= 1{\cdot}212\ 908 \ \ldots , \\ \Delta_4 &= 1{\cdot}120\ 482 \ \ldots , \end{aligned}\right\} \qquad (2\text{-}46)$$

etc.

Another interesting model for which equation (1-38) becomes solvable in a closed form follows if the internal density distribution is such that

$$\bar{\rho} = \rho_c(1 - ka^\lambda)^\mu , \qquad (2\text{-}47)$$

corresponding to

$$\rho = \rho_c(1 - ka^\lambda)^{\mu-1}\{1 - (1 + \tfrac{1}{3}\lambda\mu)ka^\lambda\} , \qquad (2\text{-}48)$$

where $\rho_c \equiv \rho(0)$ and k , λ , μ are arbitrary constants. The mass of such a configuration is going to be given by

$$m(a_1) = \tfrac{4}{3}\pi\rho_c a_1^3(1 - ka_1^\lambda)^\mu , \qquad (2\text{-}49)$$

and its finiteness makes it necessary that $\lambda\mu > 0$, in which case the external radius a_1 defined as the first zero of (2-48) follows from

$$ka_1^\lambda = \frac{1}{1 + \tfrac{1}{3}\lambda\mu} < 1 . \qquad (2\text{-}50)$$

In consequence, the density concentration of this model will be characterized by the ratio

$$\frac{\rho_c}{\rho_m} = \frac{\rho(0)}{\bar{\rho}(a_1)} = \left\{1 + \frac{3}{\lambda\mu}\right\}^\mu . \qquad (2\text{-}51)$$

This ratio becomes equal to one (i.e., the model becomes homogeneous) if either $\lambda = \infty$ or $\mu = 0$; and infinite (centrally-condensed model) only if $\lambda = 0$; for the condition $\mu = 0$ leads to a finite density concentration specified by $\rho_c/\rho_m = \exp(3/\lambda)$ which tends to infinity only as $\lambda \to 0$.

If, consistent with equations (2-47) and (2-48), we set now

$$\frac{\rho}{\bar{\rho}} = 1 - (1 + \tfrac{1}{3}\lambda\mu)ka^{\lambda} \tag{2-52}$$

and introduce this ratio in (1-38), Clairaut's equation will assume the explicit form

$$\lambda^2 x^2 (1 - x)\frac{d^2 Y_j}{dx^2} + \lambda x\{\lambda + 5 - (\lambda + 5 + 2\lambda\mu)x\}\frac{dY_j}{dx}$$
$$+ \{6 - j(j + 1) - [6 + 2\lambda\mu - j(j + 1)]x\}Y_j = 0 \ , \tag{2-53}$$

where $x \equiv ka^{\lambda}$. This is a generalized hypergeometric equation, and its particular solution which is regular at the origin is known to assume the form

$$Y_j = Aa^{j-2}F(\alpha, \beta, \gamma; ka^{\lambda}) \ , \tag{2-54}$$

where A is an integration constant,

$$\alpha, \beta, = \mu + \frac{2j + 1 \pm \sqrt{(2j + 1)^2 + 3\lambda\mu + \lambda^2\mu^2}}{2\lambda} \tag{2-55}$$

and

$$\gamma = 1 + \frac{2j + 1}{\lambda} \ . \tag{2-56}$$

As the finiteness of the mass requires that, at the surface, $x_1 \equiv ka_1^{\lambda} < 1$ the series on the right-hand side of (2-54) is absolutely convergent for all values of α , β or γ ; and the corresponding superficial distortion will be specified by

$$Y_j(a_1) = A\{3/k(3 + \lambda\mu)\}^{1/\lambda} F\{\alpha, \beta, \gamma; (1 + \tfrac{1}{3}\lambda\mu)^{-1}\} \tag{2-57}$$

and

$$\eta_j(a_1) = \left\{\frac{a}{Y_j}\frac{\partial Y_j}{\partial a}\right\}_{a_1} = j - 2$$
$$+ \frac{3\alpha\beta\lambda}{(3 + \lambda\mu)} \frac{F\{\alpha + 1, \beta + 1, \gamma + 1; (1 + \tfrac{1}{3}\lambda\mu)^{-1}\}}{F\{\alpha, \beta, \gamma; (1 + \tfrac{1}{3}\lambda\mu)^{-1}\}} \ . \tag{2-58}$$

It may be added that whenever the combination of λ and μ happens to be such that either α or β as defined by equation (2-55) becomes a negative integer, the hypergeometric series in the foregoing equations will terminate and reduce to the appropriate Jacobi polynomials.

II-3: ITERATIVE SOLUTIONS OF CLAIRAUT'S EQUATION: TERRESTRIAL AND PLANETARY CASE

In the preceding section of this monograph we have outlined some general properties of the solutions of Clairaut's or Radau's equations, and constructed some of them for certain particular distributions of density in the interior of our configurations. The aim of the present section will be to outline an iterative method by which the solution of Clairaut's equation can be constructed for any density distribution $\rho(a)$ —the rate of convergence of successive approximations becoming the higher, the lower the degree of central condensation of the distorted configuration (such as is exhibited, for instance, by the Earth or other planets of the solar system).

In order to do so, let us return to equation (1-38) and recall that, at the center (where $\rho = \bar{\rho}$), the quadratic indicial equation of (1-38) admits of the roots $-(j+3)$ and $j-2$. It is, therefore, suggestive to seek its general solution in the form

$$Y_j^i(a;\theta,\phi) = ha^{-(j+3)}G(a) + ka^{j-2}H(a) , \qquad (3-1)$$

where $G(a)$, $H(a)$ are functions regular at the origin and h, k denote suitable constants (or, rather, functions of the angular variables θ and ϕ). The first particular solution becomes infinite at the origin* and, as such, is ruled out by the initial condition (1-42); the second alone is of physical interest in this connection. We know, moreover, already from equation (2-21) that if $\rho(a) = \text{constant}$, $H(a) = 1$. Our aim of the present section will, therefore, be to construct the solution for $H(a)$ in the neighbourhood of unity, obtaining if $\rho(a)$ happens to be a slowly varying function of central distance.

In order to do so, we find it convenient to introduce an auxiliary function $\xi(a)$, depending solely on the equilibrium structure of the distorted configuration, and defined by the equation

$$\frac{m(a)}{\bar{m}(a)} = e^{-\xi(a)} \qquad (3-2)$$

as a logarithm of the ratio of the actual mass

$$m(a) = 4\pi\int_0^a \rho(a)\, a^2 da \qquad (3-3)$$

contained in a sphere of radius a to the mass

$$\bar{m}(a) = \frac{4}{3}\pi\rho(0)\,a^3 \qquad (3-4)$$

---

* For its actual construction and discussion of its properties cf., e.g., A. A. Liapounoff, Mem. de l'Acad. Sci. de St. Pétersbourg, (8) 15, No. 10, 1904.

contained there if the internal density $\rho(a)$ were constant and equal to that prevailing at the center. If so, it can be shown that the desired particular solution $H(a)$ must satisfy the integro-differential equation

$$H(a) = 1 + 2\int_0^a \frac{da}{a^{2j+2}} \int_0^a a^{j+3} \frac{d\xi}{da} \frac{d}{da}(a^{j-1}H)\,da \quad , \tag{3-5}$$

where, by (1-39) and (3-2) to (3-4),

$$\frac{d\xi}{da} = \frac{3}{a}\left\{1 - \frac{\rho}{\bar{\rho}}\right\} . \tag{3-6}$$

The merit of the transition from Y to H effected between (3-1) and (3-5) rests on the fact that, unlike the equation (1-38) governing Y, equation (3-5) for H depends on the internal structure of the distorted configuration only through the difference of $1 - (\rho/\bar{\rho})$. If, moreover, ρ happens to be a slowly varying function of a , the derivative $d\xi/da$ in the integrand on the right-hand side of (3-5) is bound to become small—zero, in fact, for a homogeneous configuration—and, as a result, the solution of this equation could be conveniently constructed by successive approximations.

In order to do so, let us rewrite equation (3-5) symbolically as

$$H(a) = 1 + 2I(H) \quad , \tag{3-7}$$

and anticipate its solution to assume the form of a series

$$H(a) = \sum_{n=0}^{\infty} H_n(a) \quad , \tag{3-8}$$

led by

$$H_0 = 1 \ . \tag{3-9}$$

As, for slowly varying ξ , the term $I(H)$ on the right-hand side of the functional equation (3-7) is likely to remain small in comparison with unity, it may be expedient to replace the exact relation (3-7) by an approximate one of the form

$$H_n(a) = 2I(H_{n-1}) \tag{3-10}$$

for $n > 0$, and to iterate the latter for successive terms of the expansion on the right-hand side of (3-8).

The first term of this series ($n = 0$) alone represents the exact solution for H if our configuration were homogeneous (in which case $\xi = 0$ and, therefore, $I(H)$ becomes identically zero). For the next term ($n = 1$) the foregoing equation (3-10) yields

$$H_1 = 2I(1) = 2\int_0^a \frac{da}{a^{2j+2}} \int_0^a a^{j+3}\frac{d\xi}{da}\frac{da^{j-1}}{da}\,da \tag{3-11}$$
$$= \frac{2(j-1)}{2j+1}\left\{\xi - \frac{1}{a^{2j+1}}\int_0^a a^{2j+1}\frac{d\xi}{da}da\right\}$$

by partial integration*; and, therefore,

$$\frac{dH_1}{da} = \frac{(2j-1)}{a^{2j+2}}\int_0^a a^{2j+1}\frac{d\xi}{da}da \ , \tag{3-12}$$

so that the function $H_1(a)$ is found to satisfy the differential equation

$$a\frac{dH_1}{da} + (2j+1)H_1 = 2(j-1)\xi \ . \tag{3-13}$$

The foregoing result can be extended by observing that, quite generally,

---

*The existence of the integral on the right-hand side requires a proof that the integral

$$I_\epsilon(1) = (j-1)\int_\epsilon^a \frac{da}{a^{2j+2}}\int_0^a a^{2j+1}\xi'\,da$$

is convergent as $\epsilon \to 0$; and this may be provided in the following way. A recourse to partial integration reveals that

$$I_\epsilon(1) = \frac{j-1}{2j+1}\left\{\int_\epsilon^a \xi' da - \frac{1}{a^{2j+1}}\int_0^a a^{2j+1}\xi' da + \frac{1}{\epsilon^{2j+1}}\int_0^\epsilon a^{2j+1}\xi' da\right\} ;$$

besides,

$$\int_0^\epsilon a^{2j+1}\xi' da < \epsilon^{2j+1}\int_0^\epsilon \xi' da = \epsilon^{2j+1}\{\xi(\epsilon) - \xi(0)\} \ .$$

Since, moreover $\xi(0) = 0$, it follows that, as $\epsilon \to 0$, the last integral on the right-hand side of the second equation will vanish, and the first two reduce indeed to the contents of the curly brackets on the right-hand side of (3-11) - Q. E. D.

$$H_n = \frac{2}{2j+1} \int_0^a a^{2-j} \frac{d}{da}(a^{j-1} H_{n-1}) \frac{d\xi}{da} da$$
$$- \frac{2}{(2j+1)a^{2j+2}} \int_0^a a^{j+3} \frac{d}{da}(a^{j-1} H_{n-1}) \frac{d\xi}{da} da \tag{3-14}$$

and, by differentiation

$$\frac{dH_n}{da} = \frac{2}{a^{2j+2}} \int_0^a a^{j+3} \frac{d}{da}(a^{j-1} H_{n-1}) \frac{d\xi}{da} da \; . \tag{3-15}$$

Therefore, for <u>any</u> value of n(>0) ,

$$a \frac{dH_n}{da} + (2j+1) H_n = 2 \int_0^a \left\{ a \frac{dH_{n-1}}{da} + (j-1) H_{n-1} \right\} \frac{d\xi}{da} da \, , \tag{3-16}$$

of which (3-13) represents a particular case.

As to the magnitude of the individual terms H_n defined by the preceding relations, it can be shown* that if

$$\Omega_n = \frac{1}{n!(j-1)a^{2j+1}} \int_0^a (2\xi)^n a^{2j} da \; , \tag{3-17}$$

then

$$H_n < \Omega_n \quad \text{and} \quad \frac{dZ_n}{da} < \frac{d\Omega_n}{da} \tag{3-18}$$

for any value of a interior to the interval $(0, a_1)$. If, moreover, the integral on the right-hand side of (3-17) is evaluated by a recourse to the Mean Value Theorem, a stronger inequality results in the form

$$H_n(a) < \frac{j-1}{2j+1} \frac{[2\xi(\alpha)]^n}{n!} \; , \tag{3-19}$$

where α denotes some value of a interior to $(0, a_1)$. As ξ is regarded to be both small and slowly varying function of a , the foregoing inequality (3-19) is often found to be quite useful.

Furthermore, it has also been shown by Liapounoff that the individual H-functions must obey the inequalities

$$1 < H_n(a) < \frac{\overline{m}(a)}{m(a)} \; , \tag{3-20}$$

---

* Cf. A. A. Liapounoff, op. cit.

where the functions $m(a)$ and $\overline{m}(a)$ are defined by our previous equations (3-3) and (3-4), and also

$$\left\{\left(\frac{a}{a_1}\right)^3 \frac{m(a_1)}{m(a)}\right\} H_n(a_1) < H_n(a) < H_n(a_1) \quad ; \qquad (3\text{-}21)$$

but for a proof of these facts the reader must be referred to Liapounoff's memoir already quoted.

All results represented by the foregoing equations (3-18)-(3-24) hold good, as they stand, only for $j > 1$. Should $j = 0$ or 1 (cases of only formal interest), special situations arise. In the case of $j = 1$, all the H_n's corresponding to $n > 0$ are identically zero, and

$$H(a) = H_0(a) = 1 \ . \qquad (3\text{-}22)$$

For $j = 0$,

$$|H_n(a)| < \Omega_n \qquad (3\text{-}23)$$

for all n's , and

$$\left|\frac{dH_n}{da}\right| < \frac{d\Omega_n}{da} , \quad \text{but} \quad \frac{dH_1}{da} = -\frac{d\Omega_1}{da} ; \qquad (3\text{-}24)$$

$H(a)$ itself may either increase or decrease, but for small values of $\underline{a}$ it will be diminishing. For $j > 1$, $H(a)$ is, however, always an increasing function of a but such, however, that the quantity

$$a^{-3} H_n(a) \int_0^a \rho a^2 da$$

is decreasing throughout the interval $(0, a_1)$.

After the digression, let us return to complete our task by constructing explicit expressions for the function $Y_j(a)$ as well as its logarithmic derivative $\eta_j(a)$ for the case of weak central condensation of the respective equilibrium configuration. As, in accordance with (3-1)

$$Y_j = ka^{j-2} H(a) , \qquad (3\text{-}25)$$

it follows that

$$\eta_j = \frac{a}{Y_j}\frac{\partial Y_j}{\partial a} = j-2 + \frac{a}{H}\frac{dH}{da} , \qquad (3\text{-}26)$$

where the function $H(a)$ can, in turn, be decomposed into a series of the form (3-8). Let us, in what follows, limit ourselves to the first two terms of this expansion, by regarding H_1 small in comparison with $H_0 = 1$. As, moreover, by (3-13)

$$\frac{a}{H_1}\frac{dH_1}{da} = -(2j+1) + \frac{2(j-1)}{H_1}\xi \ , \qquad (3\text{-}27)$$

it follows that, to the terms of first order in H_1 ,

$$\left.\begin{aligned} \eta_j(a) &= j - 2 + \frac{2(j-1)}{a^{2j+1}}\int_0^a a^{2j+1}\frac{d\xi}{da}da \\ &= j - 2 + \frac{6(j-1)}{2j+1} - \frac{6(j-1)}{a^{2j+1}}\int_0^a Da^{2j}\,da \ , \end{aligned}\right\} \qquad (3\text{-}28)$$

where we have abbreviated $D \equiv \rho/\overline{\rho}$. This expression should provide a satisfactory approximation, obtainable by quadratures, to the function $\eta_j(a)$ throughout the interior of any configuration for which the ratio D is but a slowly varying function of central distance.

II-4: ITERATIVE SOLUTIONS OF CLAIRAUT'S EQUATION: STELLAR CASE

The possibility of constructing asymptotic solutions of Clairaut's differential equation (1-38) in the form (3-5) by iteration converging rapidly for weak degrees of central condensation leads us to consider a more general process for iterative solution of Clairaut's integral equation (1-32) as it stands in the following manner. In order to do so, let us rewrite the latter in the form

$$Y = \frac{c\,a^{j+1}}{\int_0^a \rho\, a^2\, da} + J[Y] \ , \qquad (4\text{-}1)$$

where

$$\tfrac{1}{3}(2j+1)\,\overline{\rho}\,J[Y] = a^{-j-3}\int_0^a \rho\frac{\partial}{\partial a}(a^{j+3}Y)da + a^{j-2}\int_0^a \rho\frac{\partial}{\partial a}(a^{2-j}Y)da \ , \qquad (4\text{-}2)$$

and investigate the convergence of an iterative process which consists of generating successive approximations Y_n to Y by means of the relation

$$Y_n = \frac{c\,a^{j+1}}{\int_0^a \rho\, a^2\, da} + J[Y_{n-1}] \qquad (4\text{-}3)$$

in the following manner.

Let

$$|Y| < M \ , \qquad (4\text{-}4)$$

where M denotes the absolute upper bound of Y . If so, then

$$|J[Y]| < M\,J[1] \tag{4-5}$$

and as (by the Mean Value Theorem)

$$J[Y] < \frac{3}{2j+1}\,, \tag{4-6}$$

it follows that

$$|J[Y]| < \frac{3M}{2j+1}\,. \tag{4-7}$$

Now let

$$|J[Y_n - Y_{n-1}]| < \frac{3M_n}{2j+1}\,, \tag{4-8}$$

where M_n stands for the upper bound of the individual Y_n's in the interval $(0, a_1)$. If so, however, then equation (4-3) yields

$$\left.\begin{aligned} |Y_{n+1} - Y_n| &< \frac{3M_n}{2j+1} \\ &< \left(\frac{3}{2j+1}\right)^n M_1 \end{aligned}\right\} \tag{4-9}$$

and, therefore, the sequence

$$x = Y_0 + (Y_1 - Y_0) + (Y_2 - Y_1) + \ldots \tag{4-10}$$

converges absolutely and uniformly throughout the interval $(0, a_1)$ to a definite limit x .

Does this limit actually satisfy Clairaut's equation (1-38)? In order to demonstrate that this is indeed the case, let us rewrite equation (4-3) as

$$x - J[x] - \frac{c\,a^{j+1}}{\int_0^a \rho a^2 da} = x - Y_{n+1} - J[x - Y_n]\,. \tag{4-11}$$

Now if ϵ_n denotes the absolute upper bound of the differences $x - Y_n$ in the interval $(0, a_1)$, equation (4-7) reveals that

$$|J[x - Y_n]| < \frac{3\,\epsilon_n}{2j+1}\,, \tag{4-12}$$

so that

$$x - J[x] - \frac{ca^{j+1}}{\int_0^a \rho a^2 da} < \epsilon_{n+1} + \frac{3\epsilon_n}{2j+1} \quad , \tag{4-13}$$

which can be true only if the left-hand side of this inequality vanishes —i.e., if $x \equiv Y$.

The sequence of the Y_n's in terms of which we have defined x depends on the form of the adopted starting function Y_0. However, the limit x is clearly independent of it; for if an arbitrary function X_0 is used to generate another sequence of the X_n's through the mill of equation (4-3), and if—analogously with (4-9)

$$|Y_n - X_n| < \left\{\frac{3}{2j+1}\right\}^n N \quad , \tag{4-14}$$

where N represents the absolute upper bound of $J[X]$, it follows that (as $3/(2j + 1)$ is less than one for $j > 1$) the difference $Y_n - X_n$ can be diminished arbitrarily by choosing a sufficiently large value of n —no matter how large N may happen to be.

This is, of course, true in theory only; for (in the absence of an actual knowledge of N) the qualitative argument of the foregoing paragraphs cannot reveal the value of the number n of iterations necessary for attaining any pre-assigned degree of accuracy in practice. This number will clearly become the smaller, the smaller the magnitude of $|H[Y]|$ relative to the first term on the right-hand side of equation (4-1); and the conditions for which this will be so—i.e., for which the expression

$$Y \sim \frac{a^{j+1}}{\int_0^a \rho a^2 da} \tag{4-15}$$

alone can represent a satisfactory approximation to the desired particular solution of Clairaut's equation (1-38)—remain yet to be investigated.

In order to do so, let us return to the variable y related with Y by equation (2-31), which transforms (1-38) into (2-33). Let, furthermore, the surface value of $\eta(a_1) = a_1 \lambda$ (say). If so, however, the task confronting us is tantamount to a search for characteristic functions of the following linear boundary-value problem

$$L[y] = g(a)y \quad , \tag{4-16}$$

subject to the boundary conditions

$$\left.\begin{aligned} y(0) &= 0 \quad , \\ y'(a_1) &= \lambda\, y(a_1) \quad , \end{aligned}\right\} \tag{4-17}$$

where L stands for the operator

$$L \equiv \frac{d^2}{da^2} - \frac{j(j+1)}{a^2} , \tag{4-18}$$

and λ is a fixed parameter.

The operator L in (4-16) is evidently self-adjoint. Its Green's function appropriate for the given boundary conditions will, therefore, be symmetrical and of the form

$$G(a, \alpha) = -\frac{a^{j+1}}{2j+1}\{\alpha^{-j} + C_j \alpha^{j+1}\} , \quad \alpha \geq a , \tag{4-19}$$

in which we have abbreviated

$$a_1^{2j+1} C_j = \frac{j + a_1\lambda}{j - a_1\lambda + 1} . \tag{4-20}$$

Our foregoing boundary-value problem (4-16) - (4-17) can, accordingly, be rewritten in the form of the single integral equation

$$\begin{aligned}(2j+1)y(a) = &- a^{j+1} C_j \int_0^{a_1} g(\alpha)\, y(\alpha)\alpha^{j+1} d\alpha \\ &- a^{-j} \int_0^{a} g(\alpha)\, y(\alpha)\alpha^{j+1} d\alpha \\ &- a^{j+1} \int_0^{a_1} g(\alpha)\, y(\alpha)\alpha^{-j} d\alpha .\end{aligned} \tag{4-21}$$

Now in section 2 of this chapter, we found that, for homogeneous configurations $(\rho/\bar{\rho} = D = 1)$, $\eta(a) = j - 2$; while for a mass-point model ($D = 0$ for $a > 0$), $\eta(a) = j + 1$. In the former case, therefore, $\eta(a_1) = a_1\lambda = j - 2$ and, in the latter, $a_1\lambda = j + 1$ rendering the constant C_j as defined by the equation (4-20) infinite. In actual practice this limit can never be attained; for the central condensation of no existing configurations can be infinite. If it, however, happens to be high (such as is likely to be in the stars), the constants C_j may become very large indeed. The second and third term on the right-hand side of our integral equation (4-21) will then be small in comparison with the first; for this latter alone is magnified by multiplication with C_j . To the order of accuracy to which their disparity is such as to render the second and third terms ignorable, equation (4-21) should become essentially equivalent to

$$(2j+1)y(a) = -a^{j+1} C_j \int_0^{a_1} g(\alpha)\, y(\alpha)\alpha^{j+1} d\alpha ; \tag{4-22}$$

and since the limits of the integral on the right-hand side now are constant, its solution is clearly of the form

$$y(a) = A a^{j+1} , \tag{4-23}$$

when A is a constant—corresponding (by (2-32)) to

$$Y(a) = \frac{c_j a^{j+1}}{G m(a)} \tag{4-24}$$

if the constants c_j are to possess exactly the same meaning as on the right-hand side of (1-38).

In comparing the exact equation (4-21) with (4-1) and its approximant (4-22), we note that the implicit term $J[Y]$ in (4-1) will indeed tend to zero with increasing degree of central condensation (i.e., as $C_j \to \infty$). Therefore, the iterative process of solution investigated in this section should converge the more rapidly, the higher the condensation; and its first term as represented by equations (4-23) or (4-24) should constitute a good approximation to the actual solution of Clairaut's equation (1-38) in most cases encountered in stellar astrophysics.

The use of this approximate solution should, incidentally, enable us to evaluate the corresponding constants Δ_j, as defined by equation (1-36), in a more explicit form. In order to do so, it is sufficient to note that, inasmuch as equation (4-22) is homogeneous in y, its validity requires that the value of C_j involved in it be given by the equation

$$C_j^{-1} = a_1^{2j+1}(\Delta_j - 1) = -\frac{3}{2j+1}\int_0^{a_1}\left(\frac{1}{\bar{\rho}}\frac{d\rho}{da}\right) a^{2j+1}\, da . \tag{4-25}$$

A partial integration of the expression on its right-hand side reveals that

$$\begin{aligned}\int_0^{a_1}\left(\frac{1}{\bar{\rho}}\frac{d\rho}{da}\right) a^{2j+1}\, da &= -\int_0^{a_1} \rho \frac{d}{da}\left(\frac{a^{2j+1}}{\bar{\rho}}\right) da \\ &= -\int_0^{a_1} \frac{\rho}{\bar{\rho}}\left\{2j+1 - \frac{a}{\bar{\rho}}\frac{d\bar{\rho}}{da}\right\} a^{2j}\, da ;\end{aligned} \tag{4-26}$$

and as, by (1-39),

$$\frac{1}{\bar{\rho}}\frac{d\bar{\rho}}{da} = \frac{3}{a}\left\{\frac{\rho}{\bar{\rho}} - 1\right\} , \tag{4-27}$$

it follows that

$$\int_0^{a_1} \frac{1}{\bar{\rho}}\frac{d\rho}{da}\, a^{2j+1}\, da = 3\int_0^{a_1} D^2 a^{2j}\, da - 2(j+1)\int_0^{a_1} D a^{2j}\, da , \tag{4-28}$$

where, as before, $D \equiv \rho/\bar{\rho}$. For centrally-condensed configurations $D \ll 1$ and, consequently, $D^2 \ll D$. In such cases, the first integral on the right-hand side of the foregoing equation is likely to be very small in comparison with the second and may, therefore, be neglected. Doing so we arrive at the following simple equation

$$a_1^{2j+1}(\Delta_j - 1) = \frac{6(j+2)}{2j+1}\int_0^{a_1} D a^{2j} da , \tag{4-29}$$

permitting us to approximate closely the numerical values of the constants Δ_j for centrally-condensed configurations by simple quadratures of the products $a^{2j}D$ throughout the interior.

II-5: DISTURBING POTENTIAL

Throughout all developments in foregoing sections, the quantities $c_{i,j}$ specifying the disturbing potential (1-30) have so far been kept completely arbitrary; and our results should thus describe the external form or potential of fluid configurations distorted by arbitrary forces—whatever their cause may be. In order to render the solution of our hydrostatic problem uniquely determined, the nature of the forces causing distortion must now be appropriately specified. Our entire theory is, to be sure, applicable only to such forces as are derivable from a disturbing potential of the form (1-30); but these include the two most important forces of cosmic significance: namely, the centrifugal force arising from axial rotation, and tidal force produced by a neighboring mass.

The first place in order of importance among the disturbing forces deforming the shape of the Earth or the planets (though not necessarily the stars) belongs to axial rotation. If our fixed system of coordinates were such that its xy-plane would coincide with the equatorial plane of a configuration rotating with an angular velocity ω , the disturbing centrifugal potential would reduce to

$$V'_{rot} = \frac{1}{2}\omega^2 a^2 \sin^2\theta , \tag{5-1}$$

where θ stands for the co-latitude. Comparing (5-1) with (1-30) we perceive at once that a centrifugal force derived from the potential (1-30) will, to the first order in small quantities, invoke a single second-harmonic distortion, characterized by the constant

$$c_{0,2} = -\frac{1}{3}\omega^2 \tag{5-2}$$

if ω itself is constant (rigid-body rotation); and, consistent with (1-35), the external form of so rotating a configuration will (to this order of accuracy) be described by

$$Y_2^0(a_1;\theta,\phi) = -\frac{\omega^2 a_1^3}{3Gm_1}\Delta_2 P_2(\cos\theta) = -\frac{\omega^2\Delta_2}{4\pi G\rho_m}P_2(\cos\theta) , \tag{5-3}$$

where ρ_m denotes the mean density of the respective configuration. As, for the Earth,

$\omega = 7.292115 \times 10^{-5}$ rad·sec^{-1}, $a_1 = 6371.221$ km, $G = 6.668 \times 10^{-8}$ dyn·g^{-2}·cm^2, $m_1 = 5.977 \times 10^{27}$ g ($Gm_E = 3.9863 \times 10^{20}$ cm^3·sec^{-2}) and $\rho_m = 5.517$ g·cm^{-3}, it follows that

$$(Y_2^0)_{rot} = -0.00115006 \;\Delta_2 P_2(\cos\theta) \tag{5-4}$$

should represent the first-order fractional distortion due to the rotation of the Earth. As, moreover, the fractional polar flattening is known to be $(297.0 \pm 0.1)^{-1}$ from extensive geodetic measurements, a solution of the foregoing equation (5-4) for Δ_2 yields 1.9518 for a preliminary determination of this constant bearing on the internal structure of our planet.

Let us consider next a somewhat more general case of a rigid-body rotation about an axis which oscillates around a mean direction fixed in space—as the axis of the Earth does, for instance, as a result of the precession and nutation. If so, the centrifugal potential (5-1) is merely to be replaced by

$$V'_{rot} = -\frac{1}{3}\omega^2 a^2 P_2(\cos\Theta') , \tag{5-5}$$

where the angle Θ between an arbitrary radius-vector specified by the direction cosines

$$\left.\begin{aligned} \lambda &= \cos\phi\sin\theta , \\ \mu &= \sin\phi\sin\theta , \\ \nu &= \cos\theta , \end{aligned}\right\} \tag{5-6}$$

and the instantaneous axis of rotation whose direction is characterized by the direction cosines

$$\left.\begin{aligned} \lambda' &= \cos\alpha\ \sin\beta , \\ \mu' &= \sin\alpha\ \sin\beta , \\ \nu' &= \cos\beta , \end{aligned}\right\} \tag{5-7}$$

is given by

$$\cos\Theta = \lambda\lambda' + \mu\mu' + \nu\nu' . \tag{5-8}$$

As, by the addition theorem for Legendre polynomials,

$$P_2(\cos\Theta') = P_2(\nu)P_2(\nu') + \frac{1}{3}P_2^1(\nu)P_2^1(\nu')\cos(\phi - a) + \frac{1}{12}P_2^2(\nu)P_2^2(\nu')\cos 2(\phi - a) , \qquad (5\text{-}9)$$

we now have

$$\left.\begin{aligned} c_{0,2} &= -\frac{1}{3}\omega^2 P_2(\cos\beta) , \\ c_{1,2} &= +\frac{1}{9}\omega^2 P_2^1(\cos\beta)\cos(\phi - a) , \\ c_{2,2} &= -\frac{1}{36}\omega^2 P_2^2(\cos\beta)\cos 2(\phi - a) , \end{aligned}\right\} \qquad (5\text{-}10)$$

and the corresponding superficial distortion assumes the explicit form

$$(Y_2^0)_{rot} = -\frac{\Delta_2\omega^2}{4\pi G\rho_m}\left\{(1 - \frac{3}{2}\sin^2\beta)P_2(\nu) - \frac{1}{2}\sin 2\beta\cos(\phi - a)P_2^1(\nu) \frac{1}{4}\sin^2\beta\cos 2(\phi - a)P_2^2(\nu)\right\}, \qquad (5\text{-}11)$$

where the angles a and β are likely to be slowly varying functions of the time.

Lastly, let us consider the case of non-rigid rotation—such that the angular velocity ω at any point depends (say) on the distance of that point from the axis of rotation in accordance with the equation

$$\omega^2 = \sum_{m=0}^{n} \tilde{\omega}_{2m}(a\sin\theta)^{2m} , \qquad (5\text{-}12)$$

where the $\tilde{\omega}_{2m}$'s are suitable constants. In order to deduce the values of $c_{i,j}$ appropriate for this case, all we have to do is to compare the expansions of

$$V'_{rot} = \frac{1}{3}\sum_{m=0}^{n}\tilde{\omega}_{2m}(a\sin\theta)^{2(m+1)} = \sum_{j=0}^{n} c_{0,j}\, a^j P_j(\cos\theta) \qquad (5\text{-}13)$$

and equate the coefficients of the polynomials P_j of equal orders. However, in doing so we find that not all $c_{0,j}$'s will prove to be constant, but some of them become functions of a. This must, in turn, be taken account of when differentiating successively Clairaut's equation (1-32) to obtain (1-33) and (1-38)—as we shall indeed illustrate in the forthcoming section III-5.

Turning to the phenomena which can be produced by <u>tides</u>, suppose that a fluid body is acted upon by tidal forces originating from an external mass m' at a distance R from the center of gravity of our configuration. If the attracting mass is either sufficiently small—or distant—for its action to be regarded as that of a mass-point, the tidal potential V'_t reduces simply to

$$V'_t = \frac{Gm'}{\sqrt{R^2 - 2aR\cos\Theta'' + a^2}} = \frac{Gm'}{R}\sum_{j=0}^{\infty}\left(\frac{a}{R}\right)^j P_j(\cos\Theta'') + \text{a constant} \tag{5-14}$$

where Θ denotes the angle between an arbitrary radius-vector and the line joining the centers of both bodies.

The constant term on the right-hand side of (5-14) gives rise to no forces acting on the fluid globe. The term corresponding to $j = 1$ gives rise to a uniform field of force producing an acceleration of Gm'/R^2 at the origin of coordinates. We can, however, neutralize it by supposing the axes of reference to move with this acceleration. The terms with $j > 1$ constitute finally the proper tide-generating potential; and a comparison of the corresponding terms in (1-30) and (5-14) should specify the desired values of the constants $c_{i,j}$.

In order to do so, we must express again the angle Θ in terms of the spherical polar coordinates of our equatorial system; and this can be accomplished by means of the formula

$$\cos\Theta = \lambda\lambda'' + \mu\mu'' + \nu\nu'' , \tag{5-15}$$

where the direction cosines λ, μ, ν of an arbitrary radius-vector in the equatorial coordinates continue to be given by equations (5-6) while

$$\left.\begin{aligned} \lambda'' &= \cos u \cos\Omega - \sin u \sin\Omega \cos i , \\ \mu'' &= \cos u \sin\Omega + \sin u \cos\Omega \cos i , \\ \nu'' &= \sin u \sin i , \end{aligned}\right\} \tag{5-16}$$

denote the direction cosines of the line joining the centre of mass of the distorted and the disturbing body. In these latter equations u stands for the true anomaly of the disturbing body in its orbital plane; Ω, the longitude of intersection between the equator of our rotating configuration and the orbital plane of the disturbing body; and i, the angle of inclination between these two planes. A renewed appeal to the addition theorem for the Legendre polynomials will then enable us again to rewrite the polynomial $P_j(\cos\Theta'')$ on the right-hand side of (5-14) as a series in the $P_j^i(\lambda)$'s $(i \le j)$; and a comparison of this expansion with that postulated on the right-hand side of (1-30) will then specify the values of the constants $c_{i,j}$.

If, in particular, the inclination i between the equator and the orbital plane of the disturbing body were ignored,

$\cos \Theta = (\phi - u - \Omega)\sin\theta$, where all three angles ϕ, u, and Ω are now measured in the same plane. In consequence, it follows that, in this particular case, the only non-zero $c_{i,j}$'s become

$$c_{0,j} = G\frac{m'}{R^{j+1}} ; \qquad (5\text{-}17)$$

and the corresponding tidal harmonic distortion assumes, in accordance with (1-35), the form

$$Y_j^0(a_1;\theta,\phi) = \Delta_j \frac{m'}{m_1}\left(\frac{a_1}{R}\right)^{j+1} P_j\{\cos(\phi - u - \Omega)\sin\theta\} . \qquad (5\text{-}18)$$

Since, moreover, these Y_j^0's turn out to be proportional to $(a_1/R)^{j+1}$—and it is this factor which gives us primarily the right to regard the Y's as small quantities—it follows that Y_5^0 proves to be as small as $(Y_2^0)^2$, which we earlier agreed to ignore. Therefore, consistent with the order of accuracy to which we have adhered in this chapter, a description of the external form of a tidally-distorted configuration should be limited to the second, third, and fourth harmonics alone. It goes, furthermore, without saying that, consistent with (1-11), the first-order terms Y_j^i due to rotation and tides are simply additive in compounding the total distortion.

III

SECOND-ORDER THEORY

The preceding chapter of this monograph contains the outline of a method which should enable us to give explicit expressions for the form and potential of a fluid configuration subject to an arbitrary field of force, correctly to quantities of first order in superficial distortion. Having done so, our next aim will be to extend this whole theory systematically to quantities of second order in the tesseral harmonics $Y_j(a;\ \theta,\ \phi)$ arising from rotation or tides.

The technique which we shall follow to this end will be simple in principle, but rather involved in actual fact if full generality is to be retained; and the reader who will bear with us through all developments of the next two chapters will no doubt appreciate the reason why the time-lag between the first- and second-order theories has grown up to more than two centuries. Throughout the nineteenth century, the motivation for exploring the second-order terms rested solely on certain fine details of interpretation of the gravimetric measurements in geophysics (Callandreau, Darwin) and, in more recent years, with some problems connected with the internal structure of the major planets of our solar system (Jeffreys). Still more recently, the observed interaction of components in close binary systems (such as the photometric ellipticity effects, or dynamical perturbations) have provided a more powerful stimulus for investigating the second-order distortion effects. It was originally in this connection that the present writer embarked on this work; and it was completed under the impact of new problems which have since arisen when artificial satellites began revolving around the Earth in the latter part of 1957.

III-1: CLAIRAUT'S EQUATION: SECOND-ORDER TERMS

In order to embark upon our task, let us return to equation (1-15) of the preceding chapter, representing symbolically the form of the equipotential surfaces of the distorted configurations, and recall from section II-5 that its leading harmonic Y_2 proved to be a quantity of the order of ω^2 or $(a_1/R)^3$; and the subsequent harmonics Y_3 and Y_4 of tidal origin turned out to be of the order of $(a_1/R)^4$ and $(a_1/R)^5$, respectively. The squares and cross-products of the first three harmonics will, therefore, become quantities of the same order of magnitude as Y_5, Y_6, or Y_7; and a consistent second-order theory of rotational or tidal distortion must include them all. In consequence, the radius r' of any equipotential surface distorted by such forces should now be represented by

$$r' = a \sum_{j=0}^{7} Y_j(a\,;\theta\,,\,\phi) = a\,\{1 + \sum_{j=0}^{7} f_j(a)\,P_j(\theta,\phi)\} \tag{1-1}$$

correctly to terms of the order of $(a_1/R)^8$, where the coefficients f_j for $j = 0, 1$, and greater than 4 are quantities of second order.

The expansions (1-7) and (1-19) for the interior and exterior potentials U and V continue to hold good, of course, with their individual terms U_j and V_j as given by equations (1-13) or (1-14) and (1-23), respectively. In order to proceed further, the $(2-j)$th and $(j+3)$rd powers of the series (1-1) for r' occurring on the right-hand sides of equations (1-13) and (1-23) of Chapter II must be expanded in terms of the f_j's to the requisite degree of accuracy. In doing so we should remember that, of all the f_j's on the right-hand side of (1-1), only those corresponding to $j = 2$, 3, and 4 are quantities of first order. If, moreover, use is made of the well-known decomposition formula for the Legendre polynomials asserting that

$$P_m P_n = \sum_{j=0}^{m} \frac{A_{m-j}A_jA_{n-j}}{A_{m+n-j}}\left\{\frac{2m+2n-4j+1}{2m+2n-2j+1}\right\}P_{m+n-2j}\,, \tag{1-2}$$

where

$$A_j = \frac{1.3.5.\ldots(2j-1)}{j!}\,, \tag{1-3}$$

so that, in particular

$$(P_2)^2 = \frac{18}{35}P_4 + \frac{2}{7}P_2 + \frac{1}{5}P_0\,, \tag{1-4}$$

$$(P_3)^2 = \frac{100}{231}P_6 + \frac{18}{77}P_4 + \frac{4}{21}P_2 + \frac{1}{7}P_0\,, \tag{1-5}$$

and

$$P_2P_3 = \frac{10}{21}P_5 + \frac{4}{15}P_3 + \frac{9}{35}P_1\,, \tag{1-6}$$

$$P_2P_4 = \frac{5}{11}P_6 + \frac{20}{77}P_4 + \frac{2}{7}P_2\,, \tag{1-7}$$

then, consistent with (1-1) an expansion of $(r')^{j+3}$ in a series of the harmonics $P_j(\theta,\phi)$ of ascending orders assumes the explicit form

$$(r')^{j+3} = a^{j+3}\{1 + (j+3)\sum_{i=0}^{7}[f_i + (j+2)X_i]P_i\} \tag{1-8}$$

where, correctly to quantities of second order,

$$X_0 = \frac{1}{10}\{f_2^2 + \frac{5}{7}f_3 + \ldots\} , \tag{1-9}$$

$$X_1 = \frac{9}{35}f_2f_3 + \ldots , \tag{1-10}$$

$$X_2 = \frac{1}{7}\{f_2^2 + \frac{2}{3}f_3^2 + 2f_2f_4 + \ldots\} , \tag{1-11}$$

$$X_3 = \frac{4}{15}f_2f_3 + \ldots , \tag{1-12}$$

$$X_4 = \frac{9}{35}\{f_2^2 + \frac{5}{11}f_3 + \frac{100}{99}f_2f_4 + \ldots\} , \tag{1-13}$$

$$X_5 = \frac{10}{21}f_2f_3 + \ldots , \tag{1-14}$$

$$X_6 = \frac{50}{231}\{ \qquad f_3^2 + \frac{21}{10}f_2f_4 + \ldots\} , \tag{1-15}$$

$$X_7 = 0 ; \tag{1-16}$$

and, similarly,

$$(r')^{2-j} = a^{2-j}\{1 + (2-j)\sum_{i=0}^{7}[f_i + (1-j)X_i]P_i\} \tag{1-17}$$

for $j \gtrless 2$; while, for $j = 2$, the coefficient of P_2 in the expansion of

$$\log r' = \log a + \sum_{j=0}^{7} f_jP_j - \frac{1}{2}\{\sum_{j=2}^{4} f_jP_j\}^2 + \ldots \tag{1-18}$$

becomes $\{f_2 - X_2\}$.

If we insert now the foregoing expansions (1-8) and (1-17) or (1-18) in equations (1-13) and (1-14) or (1-23) of Chapter II and take advantage of the orthogonality property (1-16) of our harmonics, as given in that chapter, these equations (1-17) and (1-24) can, after a certain amount of algebra, be rewritten more explicitly as

$$U(r) = 4\pi G\sum_{j=0}^{\infty}\frac{r^jE_j(a)}{2j+1}P_j(\theta,\phi) , \tag{1-19}$$

$$V(r) = 4\pi G \sum_{j=0}^{\infty} \frac{F_j(a) P_j(\theta, \phi)}{(2j+1) r^{j+1}} , \tag{1-20}$$

where, correctly to quantities of the second order,

$$E_0 = \int_a^{a_1} \rho \frac{\partial}{\partial a} \{a^2 (\tfrac{1}{2} + f_0 + X_0)\} da , \tag{1-21}$$

$$F_0 = \int_0^a \rho \frac{\partial}{\partial a} \{a^3 (\tfrac{1}{3} + f_0 + 2X_0)\} da ; \tag{1-22}$$

while, for $j > 0$,

$$E_j = \int_a^{a_1} \rho \frac{\partial}{\partial a} \{a^{2-j} [f_j + (1-j) X_j]\} da \tag{1-23}$$

and

$$F_j = \int_0^a \rho \frac{\partial}{\partial a} \{a^{j+3} [f_j + (j+2) X_j]\} da , \tag{1-24}$$

respectively.

A determination of the functions $f_j(a)$ for fluid configurations of arbitrary density distribution $\rho(a)$ in the interior constitutes a major part of the task still confronting us. The first such function f_0 can be specified easily enough from the obvious requirement that the total mass $m_1 \equiv m(a_1)$ of our configuration must be constant and independent of distortion. For, by definition, we have, by (1-23) of Chapter II,

$$\left.\begin{aligned} m(a_1) &= \frac{1}{3} \int_0^{a_1} \rho \frac{\partial}{\partial a} \left\{ \int_0^{\pi} \int_0^{2\pi} (r')^3 \sin \theta' d\theta' d\phi' \right\} da \\ &= 4\pi \int_0^{a_1} \rho a^2 da + 4\pi \int_0^{a_1} \rho \frac{\partial}{\partial a} \{a^3 (f_0 + 2X_0)\} da ; \end{aligned}\right\} \tag{1-25}$$

and as the first term alone on the right-hand side of this last equation represents the total mass of our configuration, the second term must vanish for any form of ρ —which will be true if

$$f_0 = -2X_0 = -\frac{1}{5} f_2^2 - \frac{1}{7} f_3^2 \tag{1-26}$$

by (1-9).

The principle of the conservation of mass thus enables us to express f_0 in terms of the higher functions f_j $(j > 0)$; but in order to determine the latter, recourse must again be had to the fact that the level surfaces as represented by equation (1-1) are equipotentials. For if $V'(r)$

denotes again the disturbing potential arising from all causes, this condition will be fulfilled if

$$\Psi(r') = U(r') + V(r') + V'(r') = \text{constant} \tag{1-27}$$

over a level surface for which r' is given by (1-1).

In order to utilize this latter equation for a specification of the properties of the respective equipotentials, insert r' for r in (1-19) -(1-20), and rewrite the latter equation as

$$\left.\begin{aligned} V(r') &= 4\pi G \sum_{j=0}^{7} \frac{F_j(a)P_j(\theta,\phi)}{(2j+1)(r')^{j+1}} \\ &= 4\pi G \sum_{j=0}^{7} \mathfrak{f}_j(a)(r')^j P_j(\theta,\phi) \end{aligned}\right\} \tag{1-28}$$

correctly to the second order in small quantities. Moreover, let us assume—as in Chapter II—that the disturbing potential V' (whatever its origin) continues to be expansible in a series of the form

$$V'(r) = \sum_j c_j r^j P_j(\theta,\phi) \tag{1-29}$$

so that, over a level surface,

$$V'(r') = \sum_j c_j (r')^j P_j(\theta,\phi) \quad , \tag{1-30}$$

where the c_j's are constants (or possibly functions of a).

If so, however, then, within the scheme of our approximation, equation (1-27) can be rewritten as

$$\Psi(r') = \sum_{j=0}^{7} \left\{ 4\pi G \left(\frac{E_j}{2j+1} + \mathfrak{f}_j \right) + c_j \right\} (r')^j P_j(\theta,\phi) \quad . \tag{1-31}$$

The total potential $\Psi(r')$ can evidently remain constant over a level surface if, and only if, all terms on the right-hand side of (1-31) which depend on the angular variables θ or ϕ vanish identically—i.e., if

$$\frac{E_j(a)}{2j+1} + \mathfrak{f}_j(a) + \frac{c_j}{4\pi G} = 0 \tag{1-32}$$

for $j = 1(1)7$.

In order to determine a more explicit form of this latter equation, it is necessary to evaluate the $\mathfrak{f}_j$'s. If we insert in (1-20) for r' from (1-1), expand the resulting expressions consistently to quantities of second order, and decompose again the squares and cross-products

$P_i P_j$ into individual harmonics by means of equations (1-4) - (1-7), it follows that

$$\mathfrak{f}_0 = \left(1 + \frac{4}{5} f_2^2 + \frac{4}{7} f_3^2\right)\frac{F_0}{a} - \frac{1}{5} f_2 \frac{F_2}{a^3} - \frac{1}{7} f_3 \frac{F_3}{a^4} , \tag{1-33}$$

$$\mathfrak{f}_1 = \left(-f_1 + \frac{9}{5} f_2 f_3\right)\frac{F_0}{a^2} + \frac{F_1}{3a^3} - \frac{9}{35} f_3 \frac{F_2}{a^4} - \frac{9}{35} f_2 \frac{F_3}{a^5} , \tag{1-34}$$

$$\begin{aligned} \mathfrak{f}_2 = {} & \left(-f_2 + \frac{6}{7} f_2^2 + \frac{16}{21} f_3^2 + \frac{16}{7} f_2 f_4\right)\frac{F_0}{a^3} \\ & + \left(\frac{1}{5} - \frac{2}{7} f_2 - \frac{2}{7} f_4\right)\frac{F_2}{a^5} - \frac{4}{21} f_3 \frac{F_3}{a^6} - \frac{2}{7} f_2 \frac{F_4}{a^7} , \end{aligned} \tag{1-35}$$

$$\mathfrak{f}_3 = \left(-f_3 + \frac{9}{5} f_2 f_3\right)\frac{F_0}{a^4} - \frac{4}{15} f_3 \frac{F_2}{a^6} + \left(\frac{1}{7} - \frac{4}{15} f_2\right)\frac{F_3}{a^7} , \tag{1-36}$$

$$\begin{aligned} \mathfrak{f}_4 = {} & \left(-f_4 + \frac{54}{35} f_2^2 + \frac{72}{77} f_3^2 + \frac{80}{77} f_2 f_3\right)\frac{F_0}{a^5} \\ & - \left(\frac{18}{35} f_2 + \frac{20}{77} f_4\right)\frac{F_2}{a^7} - \frac{18}{77} f_3 \frac{F_3}{a^8} + \left(\frac{1}{9} - \frac{20}{77} f_2\right)\frac{F_4}{a^9} , \end{aligned} \tag{1-37}$$

$$\mathfrak{f}_5 = \left(-f_5 + \frac{10}{3} f_2 f_3\right)\frac{F_0}{a^6} - \frac{10}{21} f_3 \frac{F_2}{a^8} - \frac{10}{21} f_2 \frac{F_3}{a^9} + \frac{1}{11} \frac{F_5}{a^{11}} , \tag{1-38}$$

$$\begin{aligned} \mathfrak{f}_6 = {} & \left(-f_6 + \frac{400}{231} f_3^2 + \frac{40}{11} f_2 f_3\right)\frac{F_0}{a^7} - \frac{5}{11} f_4 \frac{F_2}{a^9} \\ & - \frac{100}{231} f_3 \frac{F_3}{a^{10}} - \frac{5}{11} f_2 \frac{F_4}{a^{11}} + \frac{1}{13} \frac{F_6}{a^7} , \end{aligned} \tag{1-39}$$

$$\mathfrak{f}_7 = (-f_7)\frac{F_0}{a^8} + \frac{F_7}{15a^8} . \tag{1-40}$$

The foregoing expressions for $\mathfrak{f}_j$ contain, in particular, a considerable number of the integrals F_j ($j = 2, 3, 4$), as given by equation (1-24), factored by f_2, f_3, or f_4. Since the latter f_j's are, however, known to be small quantities of first order, the F_j's multiplied by them need obviously to be evaluated only to the first order in small quantities; and equation (2-1) of Chapter II has already revealed that, to this order of accuracy,

$$\int_0^a \rho \frac{\partial}{\partial a}(a^{j+3} f_j)\,da = a^{j+1}\left\{\frac{j+1}{a} f_j - \frac{df_j}{da}\right\}\int_0^a \rho a^2\,da . \tag{1-41}$$

Inserting (1-33) - (1-40) together with (1-23) in (1-32) and making use of the foregoing relation (1-41) to simplify the results, we eventually find that, for $j > 0$,

$$f_j \int_0^a \rho a^2 da - \frac{1}{(2j+1)a^j} \int_0^a \rho \frac{\partial}{\partial a}(a^{j+3} f_j) da$$

$$- \frac{a^{j+1}}{2j+1} \int_a^{a_1} \rho \frac{\partial}{\partial a}(a^{2-j} f_j) da \tag{1-42}$$

$$= \frac{a^{j+1}}{4\pi G} c_j + R_j(a) ,$$

where, correctly to quantities of second order,

$$R_j(a) = a \frac{\partial X_j}{\partial a} \int_0^a \rho a^2 da + \frac{j+2}{(2j+1)a^j} \int_0^a \rho \frac{\partial}{\partial a}(a^{j+3} X_j) da \tag{1-43}$$

$$+ \frac{(1-j)a^{j+1}}{2j+1} \int_a^{a_1} \rho \frac{\partial}{\partial a}(a^{2-j} X_j) da ,$$

and the X_j's continue to be defined by (1-9) - (1-17).

The foregoing equation (1-42) together with (1-43) represent the desired generalization of Clairaut's equation (1-38) of Chapter II, and will hereafter be used to specify the surface form and exterior potential of distorted configurations in hydrostatic equilibrium including the second-order terms.

III-2. SURFACE FORM AND EXTERIOR POTENTIAL

In order to approach this task, let us multiply again both sides of equation (1-42) by a^j , differentiate with respect to a , and divide subsequently by a^{2j} : doing so we find that

$$\left\{ \frac{jf_j}{a^{j+1}} + \frac{1}{a^j} \frac{df_j}{da} \right\} \int_0^a \rho a^2 da - \int_a^{a_1} \rho \frac{\partial}{\partial a}(a^{2-j} f_j) da \tag{2-1}$$

$$= \frac{(2j+1)c_j}{4\pi G} + \frac{1}{a^j} \left\{ \frac{dR_j}{da} + \frac{jR_j}{a} \right\} ,$$

where the c_j's have again been regarded as constants.* A further differentiation of (2-1) with respect to a (and subsequent multiplication by a^{j+2}) yields

* A case in which the c_j's depend on a will be treated in the forthcoming section III-5.

$$a^2 \frac{d^2 f_j}{da^2} + 6 \frac{\rho}{\bar{\rho}} \left\{ a \frac{df_j}{da} + f_j \right\} - j(j+1) f_j$$
$$= \frac{3}{\bar{\rho} a^3} \left\{ a^2 \frac{d^2 R_j}{da^2} - j(j+1) R_j \right\} , \tag{2-2}$$

where $\bar{\rho}(a)$, the mean density interior to a , is given by

$$\bar{\rho}(a) = \frac{3}{a^3} \int_0^a \rho a^2 da . \tag{2-3}$$

Moreover, the logarithmic derivative

$$\eta_j(a) = \frac{a}{f_j} \left(\frac{df_j}{da} \right) \tag{2-4}$$

will, consistent with (2-2), obey the Radau first-order differential equation

$$a \frac{d\eta_j}{da} + \eta_j(\eta_j - 1) + 6 \frac{\rho}{\bar{\rho}} (\eta_j + 1) - j(j+1)$$
$$= \frac{3}{a^2 \bar{\rho} f_j} \left\{ a^2 \frac{d^2 R_j}{da^2} - j(j+1) R_j \right\} \tag{2-5}$$

generalized thus to terms of second order.

In order to put the foregoing equations to tasks set forth in the heading of this section, let us return to equation (2-1) which, for $a = a_1$, can immediately be solved for the surface values of f_j in the form

$$f_j(a_1) = \frac{(2j+1) c_j a_1^{j+1}}{G[j+\eta_j(a_1)] m_1} + \frac{S_j(a_1)}{j+\eta_j(a_1)} , \tag{2-6}$$

where

$$S_j(a) = \frac{3}{a^3 \bar{\rho}} \left\{ a \frac{dR_j}{da} + j R_j \right\} \tag{2-7}$$

and where we have abbreviated

$$m(a_1) = 4\pi \int_0^{a_1} \rho a^2 da = m_1 . \tag{2-8}$$

Now differentiating the R_j's as given by equations (1-43) with respect to a and eliminating the second derivatives of f_j with the aid of the equation (2-2) stripped of its second-order terms, we find that

$$S_1(a) = \frac{9}{35} f_2 f_3\, b_1^{(2,3)}(a) \;, \tag{2-9}$$

$$\begin{aligned} S_2(a) = {} & \frac{1}{7}\{f_2^2\, b_2^{(2,2)}(a) - \frac{3}{\bar{\rho}} \int_a^{a_1} \rho \frac{\partial}{\partial a}(f_2^2)da\} \\ & + \frac{2}{21}\{f_3^2\, b_2^{(3,3)}(a) - \frac{3}{\bar{\rho}} \int_a^{a_1} \rho \frac{\partial}{\partial a}(f_3^2)da\} \\ & + \frac{2}{7}\{f_2 f_4\, b_2^{(2,4)}(a) - \frac{3}{\bar{\rho}} \int_a^{a_1} \rho \frac{\partial}{\partial a}(f_2 f_4)da\} \;, \end{aligned} \tag{2-10}$$

$$S_3(a) = \frac{4}{15}\{f_2 f_3\, b_3^{(2,3)}(a) - 6\frac{a}{\bar{\rho}} \int_a^{a_1} \rho \frac{\partial}{\partial a}\left(\frac{f_2 f_3}{a}\right) da\} \;, \tag{2-11}$$

$$\begin{aligned} S_4(a) = {} & \frac{9}{35}\{f_2^2 b_4^{(2,2)}(a) - 9\frac{a^2}{\bar{\rho}} \int_a^{a_1} \rho \frac{\partial}{\partial a}\left(\frac{f_2^2}{a^2}\right) da\} \\ & + \frac{9}{77}\{f_3^2\, b_4^{(3,3)}(a) - 9\frac{a^2}{\bar{\rho}} \int_a^{a_1} \rho \frac{\partial}{\partial a}\left(\frac{f_3^2}{a^2}\right) da\} \\ & + \frac{20}{77}\{f_2 f_4 b_4^{(2,4)}(a) - 9\frac{a^2}{\bar{\rho}} \int_a^{a_1} \rho \frac{\partial}{\partial a}\left(\frac{f_2 f_4}{a^2}\right) da\} \;, \end{aligned} \tag{2-12}$$

$$S_5(a) = \frac{10}{21}\{f_2 f_3\, b_5^{(2,3)}(a) - 12\frac{a^3}{\bar{\rho}} \int_a^{a_1} \rho \frac{\partial}{\partial a}\left(\frac{f_2 f_3}{a^3}\right) da\} \;, \tag{2-13}$$

$$\begin{aligned} S_6(a) = {} & \frac{50}{231}\{f_3^2 b_6^{(3,3)}(a) - 15\frac{a^4}{\bar{\rho}} \int_a^{a_1} \rho \frac{\partial}{\partial a}\left(\frac{f_3^2}{a^4}\right) da\} \\ & + \frac{5}{11}\{f_2 f_4\, b_6^{(2,4)}(a) - 15\frac{a^4}{\bar{\rho}} \int_a^{a_1} \rho \frac{\partial}{\partial a}\left(\frac{f_2 f_4}{a^4}\right) da\} \;, \end{aligned} \tag{2-14}$$

$$S_7(a) = 0 \;, \tag{2-15}$$

where

$$b_j^{(i,k)}(a) = 2\eta_i \eta_k + (j+1)(\eta_i + \eta_k) + i(i+1) + k(k+1) \;, \tag{2-16}$$

and the surface values of the f_j's (for $j = 2, 3, 4$) occurring as squares or cross-products on the right-hand sides of the foregoing equations

(2-9)-(2-14) can, consistent to quantities of second order, be approximated from first-order theory by equation (2-6) stripped of its S-term. If, moreover, we particularize equation (2-9)-(2-14) for $a = a_1$ and insert for $f_j(a_1)$ we find that, correctly to the second order in small quantities, the external form of our configuration should be specified by

$$f_1(a_1) = 3\Delta_1^{(2,3)}\left(\frac{c_2 c_3 a_1^7}{G^2 m_1^2}\right), \tag{2-17}$$

$$\begin{aligned} f_2(a_1) = {} & \Delta_2\left(\frac{c_2 a_1^3}{Gm_1}\right) + \frac{5}{7}\Delta_2^{(2,2)}\left(\frac{c_2 a_1^3}{Gm_1}\right)^2 \\ & + \frac{14}{15}\Delta_2^{(3,3)}\left(\frac{c_3 a_1^4}{Gm_1}\right) \\ & \frac{18}{7}\Delta_2^{(2,4)}\left(\frac{c_2 c_4 a_1^8}{G^2 m_1^2}\right), \end{aligned} \tag{2-18}$$

$$f_3(a\ ) = \Delta_3\left(\frac{c_3 a_1^4}{Gm_1}\right) + \frac{4}{3}\Delta_3^{(2,3)}\left(\frac{c_2 c_3 a_1^7}{G^2 m_1^2}\right) + \dots, \tag{2-19}$$

$$\begin{aligned} f_4(a_1) = {} & \Delta_4\left(\frac{c_4 a_1^5}{Gm_1}\right) + \frac{5}{7}\Delta_4^{(2,2)}\left(\frac{c_2 a_1^3}{Gm_1}\right)^2 \\ & + \frac{7}{11}\Delta_4^{(3,3)}\left(\frac{c_3 a_1^4}{Gm_1}\right)^2 \\ & + \frac{100}{77}\Delta_4^{(2,4)}\left(\frac{c_2 c_4 a_1^8}{G^2 m_1^2}\right) + \dots, \end{aligned} \tag{2-20}$$

$$f_5(a_1) = \Delta_5\left(\frac{c_5 a_1^6}{Gm_1}\right) + \frac{50}{33}\Delta_5^{(2,3)}\left(\frac{c_2 c_3 a_1^7}{G^2 m_1^2}\right) \pm \dots, \tag{2-21}$$

$$\begin{aligned} f_6(a_1) = {} & \Delta_6\left(\frac{c_6 a_1^7}{Gm_1}\right) + \frac{350}{429}\Delta_6^{(3,3)}\left(\frac{c_3 a_1^4}{Gm_1}\right)^2 \\ & + \frac{225}{143}\Delta_6^{(2,4)}\left(\frac{c_2 c_4 a_1^8}{G^2 m_1^2}\right) + \dots, \end{aligned} \tag{2-22}$$

$$f_7(a_1) = \Delta_7\left(\frac{c_7 a_1^8}{Gm_1}\right) + \dots , \tag{2-23}$$

where the constants

$$\Delta_j = \frac{2j+1}{j+\eta_j(a_1)} \tag{2-24}$$

and

$$\Delta_j^{(i,k)} = \frac{b_j^{(i,k)}\Delta_j}{(i+\eta_k)(k+\eta_k)} \tag{2-25}$$

depend solely on the surface values of the various functions $\eta_j(a)$.

In order to determine these constants to the requisite degree of accuracy, recourse may be had to equation (2-5) rewritten as

$$a\frac{d\eta_j}{da} + \eta_j(\eta_j-1) + 6D(\eta_j+1) = j(j+1) + f_j^{-1}T_j(a) , \tag{2-26}$$

where we have abbreviated

$$D = \frac{\rho}{\bar{\rho}} = \frac{\rho a^3}{3\int_0^a \rho a^2 da} \tag{2-27}$$

and

$$T_j(a) = \frac{3}{a^3\bar{\rho}}\{a^2\frac{d^2R_j}{da^2} - j(j+1)R_j\} . \tag{2-28}$$

Differentiating (1-43) twice with respect to a, and eliminating again the second derivatives of f_j with the aid of equation (2-2) stripped of its second-order terms, we find that, throughout the interior (i.e., for any value of $0 \leq a \leq a_1$),

$$T_1(a) = \frac{18}{35}\{2(\eta_2\eta_3+10\eta_2+7\eta_3) - 3D(3\eta_2\eta_3+3\eta_2+3\eta_3-5)\}f_2f_3 , \tag{2-29}$$

$$\left.\begin{aligned} T_2(a) = {} & \frac{2}{7}\{2\eta_2(\eta_2+9) - 9D\eta_2(\eta_2+2)\}f_2^2 \\ & + \frac{4}{21}\{2\eta_3(\eta_3+21) - 9D(\eta_3^2+2\eta_3-2)\}f_3^2 \\ & + \frac{4}{7}\{2(\eta_2\eta_4+15\eta_2+8\eta_4) - 3D(3\eta_2\eta_4+3\eta_2+3\eta_4-7)\}f_2f_4 , \end{aligned}\right\} \tag{2-30}$$

$$T_3(a) = \frac{8}{15}\{(2\eta_2\eta_3+15\eta_2-9\eta_3) - 9D(\eta_2\eta_3+\eta_2+\eta_3)\}f_2f_3 , \tag{2-31}$$

$$\left.\begin{aligned} T_4(a) &= \frac{18}{35}\{2\eta_2(\eta_2+2) - 3D(3\eta_2^2+6\eta_2+7)\} f_2^2 \\ &+ \frac{18}{77}\{2\eta_3(\eta_3+14) - 3D(3\eta_3^2+6\eta_3+1)\} f_3^2 \\ &+ \frac{40}{77}\{(2\eta_2\eta_4+23\eta_2+9\eta_4) - 9D(\eta_2\eta_4+\eta_2+\eta_4)\} f_2 f_4 \ , \end{aligned}\right\} \quad (2\text{-}32)$$

$$T_5(a) = \frac{20}{21}\{2\eta_2(\eta_3+3) - 3D(3\eta_2\eta_3+3\eta_2+3\eta_3+5)\} f_2 f_3 \ , \quad (2\text{-}33)$$

$$\left.\begin{aligned} T_6(a) &= \frac{100}{231}\{2\eta_3(\eta_3+3) - 9D(\eta_3+2\eta_3+4)\} f_3^2 \\ &+ \frac{10}{11}\{2(\eta_2\eta_4+6\eta_2-\eta_4) - 3D(3\eta_2\eta_4+3\eta_2+3\eta_4+11)\} f_2 f_4 \ , \end{aligned}\right\} \quad (2\text{-}34)$$

$$T_7(a) = 0 \ . \quad (2\text{-}35)$$

It may be added that, as all foregoing functions $T_j(a)$ are quantities of second order, the η_j's involved on the right-hand sides of equations (2-29)-(2-35) can—within the scheme of our approximation—be replaced by the solutions of Radau's first-order equation (2-26) without the T-term. This will, however, not be true of the η_j's involved in the constants Δ_j factoring the first-order terms in f_j for $j = 2, 3, 4,$ for which a solution of the full-dress equations (2-2) or (2-5) as derived in this section becomes a necessity. And we should note in particular that—unlike (2-2)—the second-order Radau equation (2-5) depends on f_j, not only through its logarithmic derivative, but also explicitly. Therefore, the coefficients $\Delta_2, \Delta_3, \Delta_4, \ldots, \Delta_6$ will, to this order of accuracy, depend not only on the internal structure of the distorted configuration (through D), but also on the absolute amount of its first-order distortion throughout the interior.

In the light of the foregoing results, our previous expression (1-20) for the exterior potential $V(r)$ of this configuration—of primary interest to us in connection with orbit perturbations of artificial satellites—can now also be further reduced in the following way. According to equation (1-24), the coefficients $F_j(a_1)$ of the expansion on the right-hand side of (1-20) can be decomposed into

$$F_j(a_1) = \int_0^{a_1} \rho \frac{\partial}{\partial a}(a^{j+3} f_j)\, da + (j+3)\int_0^{a_1} \rho \frac{\partial}{\partial a}(a^{j+3} X_j)\, da \ . \quad (2\text{-}36)$$

The first integral on its right-hand side can, however, be solved for from Clairaut's equation (1-42) as

$$4\pi\int_0^{a_1} \rho\frac{\partial}{\partial a}(a^{j+3}f_j) = (2j+1)a_1^j m_1\{f_j(a_1) - \frac{c_j a_1^{j+1}}{Gm_1} - \frac{4\pi}{m_1}R_j(a_1)\} \qquad (2\text{-}37)$$

correctly to terms of second order; and a subsequent insertion for $R_j(a_1)$ from (1-43) reveals that

$$\frac{4\pi F_j(a_1)}{(2j+1)m_1} = f_j(a_1) - a_1\left(\frac{\partial X_j}{\partial a}\right)_{a_1} - \frac{c_j a_1^{j+1}}{Gm_1} . \qquad (2\text{-}38)$$

If, furthermore, we replace the $f_j(a_1)$'s on the right-hand side by their expression (2-6), the expansion (1-20) for the exterior potential at any point $r > a_1$ reduces to

$$V(r) = G\frac{m_1}{r}\{1 + \sum_{j=1}^{7} k_j\left(\frac{a_1}{r}\right)^j P_j(\theta, \phi)\} , \qquad (2\text{-}39)$$

where

$$k_j = (\Delta_j - 1)\left(\frac{c_j a_1^{j+1}}{Gm_1}\right) + \frac{\Delta_j}{2j+1}S_j(a_1) - a_1\left(\frac{\partial X_j}{\partial a}\right)_{a_1} \qquad (2\text{-}40)$$

correctly to terms of second order.

An inspection of the equations (1-9)-(1-16) reveals that the X_j's are quadratic in the f_j's ; and as, in general,

$$a\frac{\partial}{\partial a}(f_i f_k) = (\eta_i + \eta_k)f_i f_k , \qquad (2\text{-}41)$$

the derivatives of X_j occurring on the right-hand side of equation (2-40) can readily be evaluated.

Doing so, inserting for the $S_j(a_1)$'s from (2-9)-(2-15) and replacing, moreover, the $f_j(a_1)$'s by their expression (2-17)-(2-23) we eventually find that, for odd values of j , *

$$k_1 = + 3\Delta_{-\eta_1}^{(2,3)}\left(\frac{c_2 c_3 a_1^7}{G^2 m_1^2}\right) , \qquad (2\text{-}42)$$

$$k_3 = (\Delta_3 - 1)\left(\frac{c_3 a_1^4}{Gm_1}\right) + \frac{4}{3}\Delta_{-\eta_3}^{(2,3)}\left(\frac{c_2 c_3 a_1^7}{G^2 m_1^2}\right) , \qquad (2\text{-}43)$$

$$k_5 = (\Delta_5 - 1)\left(\frac{c_5 a_1^6}{Gm_1}\right) + \frac{50}{33}\Delta_{-\eta_5}^{(2,3)}\left(\frac{c_2 c_3 a_1^7}{G^2 m_1^2}\right) , \qquad (2\text{-}44)$$

* The second-order term of the first harmonic in the expansion (2-39) can again be removed, like the corresponding first-order term in section II-5, by allowing the axes of reference to move with this altered acceleration.

$$k_7 = (\Delta_7 - 1)\left(\frac{c_7 a_1^7}{Gm_1}\right), \tag{2-45}$$

where the constants $\Delta^{(2,3)}_{-\eta_j}$ continue to be given by equation (2-25) provided that j in the expression (2-16) for $b_j^{(i,k)}$ has been replaced by $-\eta_j(a_1)$. Moreover, when j happens to be even,

$$\begin{aligned} k_2 = (\Delta_2 - 1)\left(\frac{c_2 a_1^3}{Gm_1}\right) &+ \frac{1}{7}\{5\Delta_2^{(2,2)} - 2\eta_2\Delta_2^2\}\left(\frac{c_2 a_1^3}{Gm_1}\right) \\ &+ \frac{2}{3}\{\frac{7}{5}\Delta_2^{(3,3)} - \frac{2}{7}\eta_3\Delta_3^2\}\left(\frac{c_3 a_1^4}{Gm_1}\right)^2 \\ &+ \frac{2}{7}\{9\Delta_2^{(2,4)} - (\eta_2+\eta_4)\Delta_2\Delta_4\}\left(\frac{c_2 c_4 a_1^8}{G^2 m_1^2}\right), \end{aligned} \tag{2-46}$$

$$\begin{aligned} k_4 = (\Delta_4 - 1)\left(\frac{c_4 a_1^5}{Gm_1}\right) &+ \frac{1}{7}\{5\Delta_4^{(2,2)} - \frac{18}{5}\eta_2\Delta_2^2\}\left(\frac{c_2 a_1^3}{Gm_1}\right)^2 \\ &+ \frac{1}{11}\{7\Delta_4^{(3,3)} - \frac{18}{7}\eta_3\Delta_3^2\}\left(\frac{c_3 a_1^4}{Gm_1}\right)^2 \\ &+ \frac{20}{77}\{5\Delta_4^{(2,4)} - \eta_2+\eta_4)\Delta_2\Delta_4\}\left(\frac{c_2 c_4 a_1^8}{G^2 m_1^2}\right) \end{aligned} \tag{2-47}$$

$$\begin{aligned} k_6 = (\Delta_6 - 1)\left(\frac{c_6 a_1^7}{Gm_1}\right) &+ \frac{50}{429}\{7\Delta_6^{(3,3)} - \frac{26}{7}\eta_3\Delta_3\}\left(\frac{c_3 a_1^4}{Gm_1}\right)^2 \\ &+ \{\frac{225}{143}\Delta_6^{(2,4)} - \frac{5}{11}(\eta_2+\eta_4)\Delta_2\Delta_4\}\left(\frac{c_2 c_4 a_1^8}{G^2 m_1^2}\right) \end{aligned} \tag{2-48}$$

by which a specification of the constants in the expansion (2-39) of the exterior potential of a distorted configuration of arbitrary structure becomes complete down to the terms of the second order in its superficial deformation.

III-3. APPROXIMATE SOLUTIONS OF RADAU'S EQUATION

The second-order expressions as given in the preceding section for the external form or potential of a distorted configuration are not yet sufficiently explicit, because their coefficients Δ_j as defined by equation (2-24) involve (through $\eta_j(a_1)$) small quantities of first order, depending on the amount of distortion. In order to ascertain the extent of this dependence, let us assume that the requisite solution of Radau's second-order equation (2-26) for $\eta_j(a)$ can be decomposed into

$$\eta_j(a) = \bar{\eta}_j(a) + h_j(a) , \tag{3-1}$$

where $\bar{\eta}_j(a)$ denotes the solution of the corresponding homogeneous equation (i.e., without the T-term), and $h_j(a)$ represents the effects of distortion which we shall regard to be small enough for its squares and higher powers to be ignorable. Inserting (3-1) in (2-26) and limiting ourselves to terms of first order in $h_j(a)$, we find that this latter function must satisfy the following variational equation

$$a\frac{dh_j}{da} + (2\bar{\eta}_j + 6D - 1)h_j = \bar{f}_j^{-1}T_j(\bar{\eta}) , \tag{3-2}$$

which is linear in h_j and can, therefore, be formally shown to possess a particular integral of the form

$$h_j(a) = Q_j(\bar{\eta})\int_0^a \frac{T_j(\bar{\eta})\,da}{af_jQ_j(\bar{\eta})} , \tag{3-3}$$

where we have abbreviated

$$Q_j(\bar{\eta}) = \exp\{-\int_0^a(2\bar{\eta}_j + 6D-1)d\log a\} . \tag{3-4}$$

Now, by virtue of (2-4), it is easily seen that

$$\bar{\eta}_j \, d\log a = d\log \bar{f}_j ; \tag{3-5}$$

and, by (2-3)

$$\frac{\rho}{\bar{\rho}} = 1 + \frac{1}{3}\frac{a}{\bar{\rho}}\frac{d\bar{\rho}}{da} , \tag{3-6}$$

so that

$$(6D-1)d\log a = 5d\log a + 2d\log\bar{\rho} . \tag{3-7}$$

In consequence, by (3-4)

$$Q_j(\bar{\eta}) = a^{-5}\bar{\rho}^{-2}\bar{f}_j^{-2} \tag{3-8}$$

and, therefore,

$$h_j(a) = \frac{1}{a^5\bar{\rho}^2\bar{f}_j^2}\int_0^a T_j(\bar{\eta})\,\bar{f}_j\bar{\rho}^2a^4da . \tag{3-9}$$

As, moreover, by (2-24)

$$\Delta_j = \frac{2j+1}{j+\overline{\eta}_j(a_1)+h_j(a_1)} = \frac{2j+1}{j+\overline{\eta}_j(a_1)}\left\{1-\frac{h_j(a_1)}{j+\overline{\eta}_j(a_1)}+\dots\right\}, \quad (3-10)$$

and the $\overline{f}_j(a_1)$'s are given by equation (2-6) without the S-term it follows that

$$\Delta_j = \frac{2j+1}{j+\overline{\eta}_j(a_1)} - \frac{1}{(2j+1)a_1^{2j+1}}\left(\frac{4\pi G}{3c_j}\right)^2 \int_0^{a_1} T_j(\overline{\eta})\overline{f}_j\,\overline{\rho}^2 a^4 da \quad (3-11)$$

in which the quantities of zero and first order are separated.

In order to evaluate the first-order term on the right-hand side of (3-11), remember that, by (2-28),

$$\left.\begin{aligned}\int_0^{a_1} T_j(a) f_j \overline{\rho}^2 a\, da &= 3\int_0^{a_1}\left\{a^2\frac{d^2R_j}{da^2} - j(j+1)R_j\right\} f\overline{\rho}\, a\, da \\ &= \int_0^{a_1}\frac{d}{da}\left(\frac{\overline{\rho}S_j(a)}{a^{j-2}}\right) f\overline{\rho}\, a^{j+3} da\end{aligned}\right\} \quad (3-12)$$

by (2-7), which lends itself for partial integration to yield

$$\left.\begin{aligned}\int_0^{a_1}\frac{d}{da}\left(\frac{\overline{\rho}S_j(a)}{a^{j-2}}\right) f\overline{\rho}\, a^{j+3} da &= a_1^5\rho_m^2 f_j(a_1)S_j(a_1) \\ &\quad - \int_0^{a_1}\frac{\overline{\rho}S_j(a)}{a^{j-2}}\frac{d}{da}(f\overline{\rho}^{j+3})da\ .\end{aligned}\right. \quad (3-13)$$

But, again by (2-7),

$$\overline{\rho}S_j(a) = \frac{3}{a^{j+2}}\frac{d}{da}(a^jR_j)\ , \quad (3-14)$$

so that

$$\int_0^{a_1}\frac{\overline{\rho}S_j(a)}{a^{j-2}}\frac{d}{da}(f_j\overline{\rho}a^{j+3})da = 3\int_0^{a_1}\frac{d}{da}(a^jR_j)\frac{d}{da}(f_j\overline{\rho}a^{j+3})\frac{da}{a^{2j}}\ , \quad (3-15)$$

Integrating once again by parts we find that

$$\begin{aligned}\int_0^{a_1}\frac{d}{da}(a^jR_j)\frac{d}{da}(f_j\overline{\rho}^{j+3})\frac{da}{a^{2j}} &= \frac{R_j(a_1)}{a_1^j}\left\{\frac{d}{da}(f_j\overline{\rho}a^{j+3})\right\}_{a_1} \\ &\quad -\int_0^{a_1}\frac{R_j(a)}{a^j}\left\{\frac{d^2}{da^2}(f_j\overline{\rho}a^{j+3}) - \frac{2j}{a}\frac{d}{da}(f_j\overline{\rho}a^{j+3})\right\}da\ .\end{aligned} \quad (3-16)$$

Now

$$\frac{d}{da}(f_j\bar{\rho}a^{j+3}) = a^{j+2}f_j\bar{\rho}\,\{j + 3 + \frac{a}{f_j}\frac{df_j}{da} + \frac{a}{\bar{\rho}}\frac{d\bar{\rho}}{da}\}$$
$$= a^{j+2}f_j\bar{\rho}\{j + 3 + \eta_j + 3(D-1)\} \qquad (3\text{-}17)$$

by (2-4) and (2-27)—so that

$$\{\frac{d}{da}(f_j\bar{\rho}a^{j+3})\}_{a_1} = a_1^{j+2}\rho_m\{j + \eta_j(a_1)\}f_j(a_1) \qquad (3\text{-}18)$$

and, similarly,

$$\frac{d^2}{da^2}(f_j\bar{\rho}a^{j+3}) = a^{j+1}f_j\bar{\rho}\,\{2j(j+\eta_j) + 3[3D^2 + (2j+3)D + aD']\}. \qquad (3\text{-}19)$$

If, moreover, we make use of the relation

$$\bar{\rho}^2(aD') = \bar{\rho}\rho' - \rho\bar{\rho}' = \bar{\rho}(a\rho') - 3\rho(\rho - \bar{\rho}) \quad , \qquad (3\text{-}20)$$

deduced from a differentiation of (2-27), it follows that

$$\left.\begin{aligned}\left\{\frac{d^2}{da^2} - \frac{2j}{a}\frac{d}{da}\right\}(f\bar{\rho}a^{j+3}) &= 9a^{j+1}f_j\bar{\rho}\,\{3D(D-1) + aD'\}\\ &= 9a^{j+2}f_j(\frac{d\rho}{da}) \quad .\end{aligned}\right\} \qquad (3\text{-}21)$$

Collecting the relevant results from equations (3-12)-(3-21) we eventually establish that

$$\begin{aligned}\int_0^{a_1} T_j(a)f_j\bar{\rho}^2a^4\,da &= a_1^5\rho_m^2 f_j(a_1)S_j(a_1)\\ &- 3a_1^2\rho_m\{j + \overline{\eta}_j(a_1)\}f_j(a_1)R_j(a_1) \qquad (3\text{-}22)\\ &+ 27\int_0^{a_1} a^2 f_j R_j\frac{d\rho}{da}da \quad ,\end{aligned}$$

which by use of (2-16) and of the fact that

$$\rho_m = \frac{3m_1}{4\pi a_1^3} \qquad (3\text{-}23)$$

permits us to rewrite (3-22) in the form

$$\Delta_j = \frac{2j+1}{j+\bar{\eta}_j(a_1)} - \frac{Gm_1}{c_j a_1^{j+1}}\left\{\frac{S_j(a_1)}{j+\eta_j(a_1)} - \frac{4\pi R_j(a_1)}{m_1}\right\}$$

$$- \frac{3a_1}{2j+1}\left(\frac{4\pi G}{c_j a_1^{j+1}}\right)^2 \int_0^{a_1} \rho \frac{\partial}{\partial a}(a^2 f_j R_j)da \qquad (3\text{-}24)$$

which is better suited for numerical computation.

The foregoing result holds good for fluid configuration of any arbitrary structure. If, however, its density concentration is high (such as is likely to be characteristic of the stars), our results can be given much more explicit form. In order to do so let us recall that, in accordance with the result established in section II-4, the functions $f_j(a)$ can in such a case be closely approximated by the simple expressions

$$\bar{f}_j(a) = \frac{3c_j}{4\pi G\bar{\rho}} a^{j-2} \quad ; \qquad (3\text{-}25)$$

and if we insert this on the right-hand side of equation (3-15) can be evaluated in a closed form to yield

$$\int_0^{a_1} \frac{d}{da}(a^j R_j)\frac{d}{da}(f_j \bar{\rho} a^{j+3})\frac{da}{a^{2j}} = \frac{3(2j+1)}{4\pi G} c_j a_1^j R_j(a_1) \ , \qquad (3\text{-}26)$$

where the surface values of $R_j(a_1)$ are obtainable from (1-43).

In order to ascertain them, let us recall that

$$R_j(a_1) = \frac{a_1 m_1}{4\pi}\left(\frac{\partial X_j}{\partial a}\right)_1 + \frac{j+2}{(2j+1)a_1^j}\int_0^{a_1} \rho \frac{\partial}{\partial a}(a^{j+3}X_j)da \ , \qquad (3\text{-}27)$$

where m_1 denotes the total mass of our configuration, and the X_j's continue to be given by equations (1-9) - (1-16) as appropriate linear combinations of the cross-products $f_i f_j$. Approximating the latter by (3-25) and making use of (2-41), where (by a logarithmic differentiation of equation (4-24) of Chapter II) $\bar{\eta}_j(a_1) = j + 1$ on the surface, we eventually establish that

$$\left\{\frac{\partial}{\partial a}(f_2^2)\right\}_{a_1} = \frac{54}{a_1 \rho_m^2}\left(\frac{c_2}{4\pi G}\right)^2 \ , \qquad (3\text{-}28)$$

$$\left\{\frac{\partial}{\partial a}(f_3^2)\right\}_{a_1} = \frac{9a_1}{2\rho_m^2}\left(\frac{c_3}{\pi G}\right)^2 \ , \qquad (3\text{-}29)$$

$$\left\{\frac{\partial}{\partial a}(f_2 f_3)\right\}_{a_1} = \frac{63}{\rho_m^{\ 2}}\left(\frac{c_2 c_3}{16\pi^2 G^2}\right) , \tag{3-30}$$

$$\left\{\frac{\partial}{\partial a}(f_2 f_4)\right\}_{a_1} = \frac{9a_1}{2\rho_m^{\ 2}}\left(\frac{c_2 c_4}{\pi^2 G^2}\right) , \tag{3-31}$$

where $\rho_m \equiv \bar{\rho}(a_1)$. Therefore,

$$\frac{a_1 m_1}{4\pi}\left(\frac{\partial X_2}{\partial a}\right)_1 = \frac{2a_1^3}{7(4\pi G)^2 \rho_m}\{9c_2^2 + 8(c_3^2 + 3c_2 c_4)a_1^2\} , \tag{3-32}$$

$$\frac{a_1 m_1}{4\pi}\left(\frac{\partial X_3}{\partial a}\right)_1 = \frac{28\, c_2 c_3 a_1^4}{5(4\pi G)^2 \rho_m} , \tag{3-33}$$

$$\frac{a_1 m_1}{4\pi}\left(\frac{\partial X_4}{\partial a}\right)_1 = \frac{6a_1^3}{385(4\pi G)^2 \rho_m}\{297c_2^2 + 20(9c_3^2 + 20c_2 c_4)a_1^2\}, \tag{3-34}$$

$$\frac{a_1 m_1}{4\pi}\left(\frac{\partial X_5}{\partial a}\right)_1 = \frac{10c_2 c_3 a_1^4}{(4\pi G)^2 \rho_m} , \tag{3-35}$$

$$\frac{a_1 m_1}{4\pi}\left(\frac{\partial X_6}{\partial a}\right)_1 = \frac{40a_1^5}{77(4\pi G)^2 \rho_m}\{10c_3^2 + 21c_2 c_4\} , \tag{3-36}$$

etc.

On the other hand, by virtue of (3-25), as well as of equation (3-6),

$$(4\pi G)^2 \int_0^{a_1} \rho \frac{\partial}{\partial a}(a^{j+3} f_k f_\ell)da$$

$$= 9(j+k+\ell+5)c_k c_\ell \int_0^{a_1} (\rho/\bar{\rho}^2)a^{j+k+\ell-2}da \tag{3-37}$$

$$- 54c_k c_\ell \int_0^{a_1} (\rho^2/\bar{\rho}^3)a^{j+k+\ell-2}da ;$$

and, if $\rho/\bar{\rho} \ll 1$, the second term on the right-hand side of the foregoing equation will again be small in comparison with the first, and may hereafter be ignored. If so, then abbreviating

$$\frac{\rho(a)}{\bar{\rho}(a)} = D \quad \text{and} \quad \frac{\bar{\rho}(a_1)}{\bar{\rho}(a)} = \tilde{D} , \tag{3-38}$$

the integral on the left-hand side of (3-37) can be satisfactorily approximated by

$$\left.\begin{aligned}\int_0^{a_1} \rho \frac{\partial}{\partial a}(a^{j+3} f_k f_\ell)\,da &= \frac{9(j+k+\ell+5)}{(4\pi G)^2 \rho_m} c_k c_\ell \int_0^{a_1} D\tilde{D} a^{j+k+\ell-2}\,da \\ &= a_1^{\,j+k+\ell-1}\left\{\frac{c_k c_\ell}{(4\pi G)^2 \rho_m}\right\} K_j^{(k,\ell)} ,\end{aligned}\right\} \quad (3\text{-}39)$$

and the values of the coefficients $K_j^{(k,\ell)}$ can be readily ascertained by quadratures.

Having determined them, and inserted together with (3-32)-(3-36) in equation (3-27) for $R_j(a_1)$, we eventually find that, for odd values of $j > 1$,

$$(4\pi G)^2 \rho_m R_3(a_1) = \frac{4a_1^4}{105}\{147 + 5K_3^{(2,3)}\} c_2 c_3 , \quad (3\text{-}40)$$

$$(4\pi G)^2 \rho_m R_5(a_1) = \frac{10a_1^4}{33}\{33 + K_5^{(2,3)}\} c_2 c_3 ; \quad (3\text{-}41)$$

while for even j's it follows that

$$\begin{aligned}(4\pi G)^2 \rho_m R_2(a_1) &= \frac{2a_1^3}{33}\{45 + 2K_2^{(2,2)}\} c_2^2 \\ &+ \frac{8a_1^5}{105}\{30 + K_2^{(3,3)}\} c_3^2 \\ &+ \frac{8a_1^5}{35}\{30 + K_2^{(2,4)}\} c_2 c_4 ,\end{aligned} \quad (3\text{-}42)$$

$$\begin{aligned}(4\pi G)^2 \rho_m R_4(a_1) &= \frac{6a_1^3}{35}\{27 + K_4^{(2,2)}\} c_2^2 \\ &+ \frac{6a_1^5}{77}\{36 + K_4^{(3,3)}\} c_3^2 \\ &+ \frac{40a_1^5}{231}\{36 + K_4^{(2,4)}\} c_2 c_4 ,\end{aligned} \quad (3\text{-}43)$$

and

$$\begin{aligned}(4\pi G)^2 \rho_m R_6(a_1) &= \frac{400a_1^5}{3003}\{39 + K_6^{(3,3)}\} c_3^2 \\ &+ \frac{40a_1^5}{143}\{39 + K_6^{(2,4)}\} c_2 c_4 .\end{aligned} \quad (3\text{-}44)$$

Lastly, if we take again advantage of the fact that, within the scheme of our approximation, $\eta_j(a_1) = j + 1$ and combine it with (2-16), equations (2-9)-(2-15) at $a = a_1$ assume the more explicit forms

$$S_2(a_1) = \frac{48}{7}\left(\frac{c_2 a_1^3}{Gm_1}\right)^2 + \frac{160}{21}\left(\frac{c_3 c_1^4}{Gm_1}\right)^2 + \frac{160}{7}\left(\frac{c_2 c_4 a_1^8}{G^2 m_1^2}\right) , \tag{3-45}$$

$$S_3(a_1) = \frac{56}{3}\left(\frac{c_2 c_3 a_1^7}{G^2 m_1^2}\right) , \tag{3-46}$$

$$S_4(a_1) = \frac{108}{7}\left(\frac{c_2 a_1^3}{Gm_1}\right)^2 + \frac{864}{77}\left(\frac{c_3 a_1^4}{Gm_1}\right)^2 + \frac{1920}{77}\left(\frac{c_2 c_4 a_1^8}{G^2 m_1^2}\right), \tag{3-47}$$

$$S_5(a_1) = 40\left(\frac{c_2 c_3 a_1^7}{G^2 m_1^2}\right) , \tag{3-48}$$

$$S_6(a_1) = \frac{800}{33}\left(\frac{c_3 a_1^4}{Gm_1}\right)^2 + \frac{560}{11}\left(\frac{c_2 c_4 a_1^8}{G^2 m_1^2}\right) . \tag{3-49}$$

If we insert now the results represented by equations (3-40)-(3-44) and (3-45)-(3-49) in equation

$$\Delta_j = \frac{2j+1}{j + \bar{\eta}_j(a_1)} - \frac{Gm_1}{c_j a_1{}^{j+1}} \left\{ \frac{S_j(a_1)}{2j+1} - \frac{4\pi R_j(a_1)}{m_1} \right\} , \tag{3-50}$$

obtaining from (3-24) for the case considered in this section, we find eventually that

$$\begin{aligned} \Delta_2 = \frac{5}{2+\bar{\eta}_2} &- \frac{18}{35}\left(\frac{c_2 a_1^3}{Gm_1}\right)\{1 - \frac{2}{27}K_2{}^{(2,2)}\} \\ &- \frac{16}{21}\left(\frac{c_3^2 a_1{}^5}{c_2 Gm_1}\right)\{1 - \frac{1}{30}K_2{}^{(3,3)}\} \\ &- \frac{16}{7}\left(\frac{c_4 a_1{}^5}{Gm_1}\right)\{1 - \frac{1}{30}K_2{}^{(2,4)}\} , \end{aligned} \tag{3-51}$$

$$\Delta_3 = \frac{7}{3+\bar{\eta}_3} - \frac{4}{5}\left(\frac{c_2 a_1^3}{Gm_1}\right) \{1 - \frac{5}{63}K_3{}^{(2,3)}\} , \tag{3-52}$$

$$\Delta_4 = \frac{9}{4+\bar{\eta}_4} - \frac{6}{35}\left(\frac{c_2^2 a_1}{Gm_1}\right)\{1 - \frac{1}{3}K_4^{(2,2)}\}$$

$$- \frac{24}{77}\left(\frac{c_3^2 a_1^3}{c_4 Gm_1}\right)\{1 - \frac{1}{12}K_4^{(3,3)}\} \qquad (3\text{-}53)$$

$$- \frac{160}{3.77}\left(\frac{c_2 a_1^3}{Gm_1}\right)\{1 - \frac{1}{12}K_4^{(2,4)}\} ,$$

$$\Delta_5 = \frac{11}{5+\bar{\eta}_5} - \frac{10}{35}\left(\frac{c_2 c_3 a_1}{c_5 Gm_1}\right)\{1 - \frac{1}{3}K_5^{(2,3)}\} , \qquad (3\text{-}54)$$

$$\Delta_6 = \frac{13}{6+\bar{\eta}_6} - \frac{400}{7.13.33}\left(\frac{c_3^2 a_1}{c_6 Gm_1}\right)\{1 - \frac{1}{3}K_6^{(3,3)}\}$$

$$- \frac{40}{11.13}\left(\frac{c_2 c_4 a_1}{c_6 Gm_1}\right)\{1 - \frac{1}{3}K_6^{(2,4)}\} , \qquad (3\text{-}55)$$

where $\bar{\eta}_j$ continues to denote the surface value $(a = a_1)$ of the function defined by Radau's equation (1-40) of Chapter II and subject to the initial condition (1-41) of that chapter. It may also be noted that if all the coefficients $K_j^{(k,\ell)}$ were zero, the foregoing expressions for Δ_j would reduce to those appropriate for the mass-point model; the terms involving $K_j^{(k,\ell)}$ represent, therefore, the net effect of the finite degree of central condensation in this connection.

III-4: EQUILIBRIUM TIDES

Throughout all foregoing developments of the present chapter, the constants c_j specifying the nature of distortion have again so far been kept completely arbitrary; and our results should, therefore, describe the external form or potential of fluid configurations distorted by arbitrary forces—whatever their cause. In particularizing these results to the forces which determine the form of the Earth or the stars, let us consider first the problem of the equilibrium tides—not because such tides would necessarily be the primary cause of such a distortion, but because their analytic treatment is connected more closely with the developments of the preceding sections than that of polar flattening.

In order to determine the values of the constants c_j appropriate for tidal distortion of a fluid body of mass m_1 by that of mass m_2 correctly to quantities of second order, let us recall that, in accordance with equations (1-49) and (5-17) of Chapter II, the exterior potential of the mass m_1 at any point $r > a_1$ from its center will be given by

$$V(r) = G\frac{m_1}{r}\left\{1 + \frac{m_2}{m_1}\sum_{j=2}^{4}\left(\frac{a_1}{R}\right)^{j+1}\left(\frac{a_1}{r}\right)^{j}(\Delta_{j,1}-1)P_j(\lambda)\right\} \qquad (4-1)$$

where λ denotes the cosine of an angle between the radius-vector r and the line R joining the centers of the two bodies (cf. the accompanying Figure 3-1). As, to the foregoing degree of accuracy, the disturbing effect of m_2 on m_1 was found (cf. again section II-5) to be tantamount to that of a mass-point, the tide-generating potential V' of the configuration of mass m_2 on that of mass m_1 should be obtainable from (4-1) by a mere interchange of indices as

$$V'(r_2) = G\frac{m_2}{r_2}\left\{1 + \frac{m_1}{m_2}\sum_{j=2}^{4}\left(\frac{a_2}{R}\right)^{j+1}\left(\frac{a_2}{r_2}\right)^{j}(\Delta_{j,2}-1)P_j(\lambda')\right\}, \qquad (4-2)$$

where r_2 denotes the distance of an arbitrary point of mass m_1 from the center of m_2, and the cosines λ, λ' of the angles between R and r or r_2 are (cf. again Fig. 3-1) given by the equations

$$\left.\begin{aligned} r^2 &= R^2 + r_2^2 - 2Rr_2\lambda\ , \\ r_2^2 &= R^2 + r^2 - 2Rr\lambda\ . \end{aligned}\right\} \qquad (4-3)$$

The constants $\Delta_{j,2}$ refer then to the internal structure of the disturbing configuration of mass m_2 .

Eliminating r_2 between equations (4-3) and solving for λ' we find that

$$\lambda' = \frac{R - \lambda r}{\sqrt{R^2 + r^2 - 2Rr\lambda}} = \left\{1 - \frac{r\lambda}{R}\right\}\sum_{j=0}^{\infty}\left(\frac{r}{R}\right)^{j}P_j(\lambda)\ ; \qquad (4-4)$$

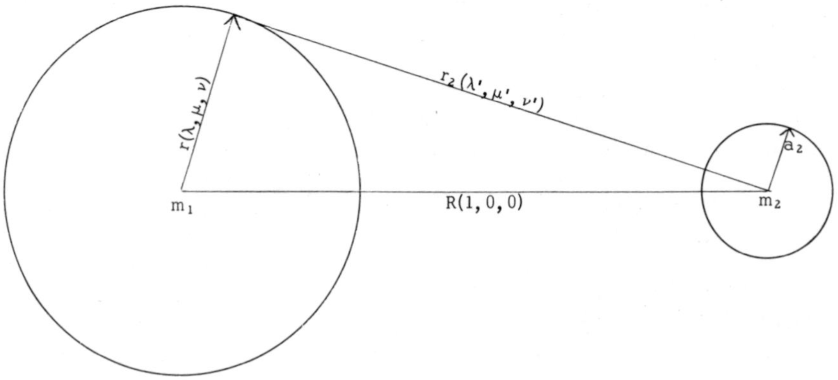

Figure 3-1

and making use of the decomposition theorem (1-2) for Legendre polynomials we find it easy to show that

$$\lambda' = 1 + \sum_{j=1}^{\infty} \frac{j}{2j+1} \{P_{j+1}(\lambda) - P_{j-1}(\lambda)\}(\frac{r}{R})^{j+1} . \tag{4-5}$$

Hence,

$$P_2(\lambda') = 1 + (\frac{r}{R})^2 \{P_2(\lambda) - P_0(\lambda)\} + \ldots \tag{4-6}$$

and

$$P_3(\lambda') = P_4(\lambda') = 1 \tag{4-7}$$

as far as we are concerned.

On the other hand, as

$$\frac{1}{r^2} = \frac{1}{\sqrt{R^2 + r^2 - 2Rr\lambda}} = \frac{1}{R} \sum_{j=0}^{\infty} (\frac{r}{R})^j P_j(\lambda) , \tag{4-8}$$

it follows that

$$(\frac{R}{r_2})^3 = 1 + 3(\frac{r}{R}) P_1(\lambda) + (\frac{r}{R})^2[5P_2(\lambda)+1] + \ldots , \tag{4-9}$$

$$(\frac{R}{r_2})^4 = 1 + 4(\frac{r}{R})P_1(\lambda) + \ldots , \tag{4-10}$$

etc. If we insert now the foregoing expressions for the inverse powers of r_2 together with (4-6) and (4-7) in equation (4-2), the disturbing potential V' rewritten in terms of the r, λ - variables will assume the more explicit form

$$\begin{aligned} V'(r) = {} & G\frac{m_2}{R} \sum_{j=0}^{7} (\frac{r}{R})^j P_j(\lambda) \\ & + G\frac{m_1}{R}(\Delta_{22} - 1)(\frac{a_2}{R})^5 \{1 + 3(\frac{r}{R})P_1(\lambda) + 6(\frac{r}{R})^2 P_2(\lambda) + \ldots\} \\ & + G\frac{m_1}{R}(\Delta_{23} - 1)(\frac{a_2}{R})^7 \{1 + \ldots\} + \ldots , \end{aligned} \tag{4-11}$$

within the scheme of our approximation.

The last step in our reductions should consist of the specification of the disturbing potential V' over an arbitrary level surface of the distorted configuration; and this is accomplished simply by identifying r with r' as defined by equation (1-1). Doing so we find that the corresponding potential $V'(r')$ should indeed be expansible in a series of the form

$$V'(r') = \sum_{j=0}^{\infty} c_j (r')^j P_j(\lambda) , \tag{4-12}$$

consistent with (1-30), where according to (4-11)

$$c_2 = G\frac{m_2}{R^3} + 6G(\Delta_{2,2} - 1)\frac{m_1}{R^3}(\frac{a_2}{R})^5 \tag{4-13}$$

and, for $j > 2$,

$$c_j = Gm_2 R^{-j-1} . \tag{4-14}$$

From these results it readily transpires that the fractional dimensions (and internal structure) of the disturbing body of mass m_2 begins to affect the distortion of the configuration of mass m_1 through a second-harmonic term with the coefficient $a_1^3 a_2^5/R^8$; for all terms of lesser orders (i.e., up to a^8/R^8) the tidal action of one body upon another can still be regarded as that of a mass point. As, moreover, it follows from (4-13) and (4-14) that, within the scheme of our approximation,

$$c_2 c_4 = c_3^2 , \tag{4-15}$$

equations (2-17)-(2-23) governing the external form of a tidally-distorted configuration assume now the more explicit forms

$$f_1(a_1) = 3\Delta_1^{(2,3)}(\frac{m_2}{m_1})^2(\frac{a_1}{R})^7 , \tag{4-16}$$

$$\begin{aligned} f_2(a_1) = {} & \Delta_2(\frac{m_2}{m_1})(\frac{a_1}{R})^3 + \frac{5}{7}\Delta_2^{(2,2)}(\frac{m_2}{m_1})^2(\frac{a_1}{R})^6 \\ & + \{\frac{14}{15}\Delta_2^{(3,3)} + \frac{18}{7}\Delta_2^{(2,4)}\}(\frac{m_2}{m_1})^2(\frac{a_1}{R})^8 \\ & + 6\Delta_2(\Delta_{2,2} - 1)(\frac{a_1}{R})^3(\frac{a_2}{R})^5 , \end{aligned} \tag{4-17}$$

$$f_3(a_1) = \Delta_3\frac{m_2}{m_1}(\frac{a_1}{R})^4 + \frac{4}{3}\Delta_3^{(2,3)}(\frac{m_2}{m_1})^2(\frac{a_1}{R})^7 , \tag{4-18}$$

$$f_4(a_1) = \Delta_4 \frac{m_2}{m_1}(\frac{a_1}{R})^5 + \frac{5}{7}\Delta_4^{(2,2)}(\frac{m_2}{m_1})^2(\frac{a_1}{R})^6$$
$$+ \{\frac{7}{11}\Delta_4^{(3,3)} + \frac{100}{77}\Delta_4^{(2,4)}\}(\frac{m_2}{m_1})^2(\frac{a_1}{R})^8 , \tag{4-19}$$

$$f_5(a_1) = \Delta_5 \frac{m_2}{m_1}(\frac{a_1}{R})^6 + \frac{50}{33}\Delta_5^{(2,3)}(\frac{m_2}{m_1})^2(\frac{a_1}{R})^7 , \tag{4-20}$$

$$f_6(a_1) = \Delta_6 (\frac{m_2}{m_1})(\frac{a_1}{R})^7 + \{\frac{350}{429}\Delta_6^{(3,3)} + \frac{225}{143}\Delta_6^{(2,4)}\}(\frac{m_2}{m_1})^2(\frac{a_1}{R})^8, \tag{4-21}$$

$$f_7(a_1) = \Delta_7 (\frac{m_2}{m_1})(\frac{a_1}{R})^8 + \dots , \tag{4-22}$$

where, it should be remembered (cf. equations 3-24 or, for centrally-condensed configurations, 3-51 to 3-55), the coefficients Δ_j in the leading terms of these expansions contain small quantities of first order.

Moreover, the coefficients k_j in our expansion (2-39) of the exterior potential of a tidally-distorted configuration of arbitrary structure can likewise be obtained from equations (2-42)-(2-48) by inserting for c_j from (4-13) and (4-14); but the actual algebra can be left as an exercise for the interested reader.

This completes our present study of the quantitative properties of compressible fluid configurations, of arbitrary internal structure, distorted by the tidal forces to terms of second order. Our next task should be to investigate, to the same order of accuracy, the effects produced by axial rotation; and this we shall undertake in the following section III-5.

III-5: ROTATIONAL EFFECTS

In considering the effects of purely rotational distortion, let us identify the xy-plane of our frame of reference with the equatorial plane of our rotating configuration, and let θ denote the angle between an arbitrary radius-vector and the z-axis (coinciding with the axis of rotation). The expression (1-1) for the radius r' of any equipotential surface should then reduce to

$$r' = a\{1 + f_0 + f_2 P_2(\nu) + f_4 P_4(\nu) + \dots\} , \tag{5-1}$$

where $\nu \equiv \cos\theta$, and the quantities f_0 and f_4 are of second order.

Up to a certain point, the whole analysis of the rotational problem becomes a particular case of the theory developed already in Section III-1. As the functions f_1, f_3, f_5, ... are identically zero, the only non-vanishing X_j's are then particular cases of (1-9), (1-11), and (1-13), of the form

$$X_0 = \frac{1}{10} f_2^2 , \tag{5-2}$$

$$X_2 = \frac{1}{7} f_2^2 , \tag{5-3}$$

$$X_4 = \frac{9}{35} f_2^2 , \tag{5-4}$$

and the appropriate versions of equations (1-35) and (1-37) become

$$f_2 = \{-f_2 + \frac{6}{7} f_2^2\} \frac{F_0}{a^3} + \{\frac{1}{5} - \frac{2}{7} f_2\} \frac{F_2}{a^5} , \tag{5-5}$$

$$f_4 = \{-f_4 + \frac{54}{35} f_2^2\} \frac{F_0}{a^5} - \frac{18}{35} f_2 \frac{F_2}{a^7} + \frac{F_4}{9a^9} , \tag{5-6}$$

respectively, where F_0, F_2, F_4 continue to be given by equations (1-22) and (1-24).

The disturbing potential V' arising from rigid-body rotation with a constant angular velocity ω will be of the form

$$V'(r') = \frac{1}{2} \omega^2 r'^2 \sin^2 \theta = \frac{1}{3} \omega^2 r'^2 \{1 - P_2(\nu)\} , \tag{5-7}$$

where

$$\begin{aligned} r'^2 &= a^2 \{1 + 2f_2 P_2(\nu) + \ldots \} \\ &= a^2 + 2f_2 r'^2 P_2(\nu) + \text{higher-order terms;} \end{aligned} \tag{5-8}$$

and this will be of the form (1-30) if

$$c_0 = \frac{1}{3} \omega^2 a^2 \tag{5-9}$$

and

$$c_2 = -\frac{1}{3} \omega^2 (1 - 2f_2) \tag{5-10}$$

which—unlike those given by equations (4-13) and (4-14) in the case of a purely tidal distortion—now become functions of a .

The fact that this is so makes it necessary to differentiate the c_j's in passing from (1-42) to (2-1) and to generalize the latter to the form

$$\left\{jf_j + a\frac{df_j}{da}\right\}\int_0^a \rho\, a^2 da - a^{j+1}\int_a^{a_1} \rho\frac{\partial}{\partial a}(a^{2-f} f_j)da$$
$$= \frac{a^{j+1}}{4\pi G}\left\{a\frac{dc_j}{da} + (2j+1)c_j\right\} + (a^{2-j} f_j)\left\{\frac{dR_j}{da} + \frac{jR_j}{a}\right\}, \tag{5-11}$$

and equation (2-2) should then likewise become

$$a^2 \frac{d^2 f_j}{da^2} + 6\frac{\rho}{\bar\rho}\left\{a\frac{df_j}{da} + f_j\right\} - j(j+1)f_j$$
$$= \frac{3a^j}{4\pi G\bar\rho}\left\{\frac{d^2 c_j}{da^2} + 2\frac{j+1}{a}\frac{dc_j}{da}\right\} + \frac{3}{a^3\bar\rho}\left\{a^2\frac{d^2 R_j}{da^2} - j(j+1)R_j\right\}. \tag{5-12}$$

Moreover, equation (2-6) should, by virtue of (5-11), be augmented to read

$$f_j(a_1) = \frac{1}{j+\eta_j(a_1)}\left\{\frac{a_1^{j+1}}{Gm_1}\left[a\frac{dc_j}{da} + (2j+1)c_j\right] + S_j(a_1)\right\}. \tag{5-13}$$

Now, consistent with (5-10)

$$a\frac{dc_2}{da} = \frac{2}{3}a\omega^2\frac{df_2}{da} = \frac{2}{3}\omega^2 f_2\eta_2 , \tag{5-14}$$

and

$$a^2\frac{d^2 c_2}{da^2} = 4\omega^2 f_2\{1 - D(\eta_2+1)\} \tag{5-15}$$

by virtue of Radau's differential equation, so that

$$a\frac{dc_2}{da} + 5c_2 = -\frac{5}{3}\omega^2 + \frac{2}{3}\omega^2 f_2(\eta_2+5) \tag{5-16}$$

and

$$a^2\frac{d^2 c_2}{da^2} + 6a\frac{dc_2}{da} = 4\omega^2 f_2(1 - D)(\eta_2+1) \tag{5-17}$$

where, as before, $D \equiv \rho/\bar\rho$.

Hence, equation (5-13) reveals that, more explicitly,

$$f_2(a_1) = \frac{-5}{2+\eta_2}\left(\frac{\omega^2 a_1^3}{3Gm_1}\right) - \frac{20}{7}\left\{\frac{\bar\eta_2^{\,2}+17\bar\eta_2+20}{(\bar\eta_2+2)^3}\right\}\left(\frac{\omega^2 a_1^3}{3Gm_1}\right)^2, \tag{5-18}$$

and

$$f_4(a_1) = \frac{90}{7}\left\{\frac{3+\bar{\eta}_2}{(2+\bar{\eta}_2)(4+\bar{\eta}_4)}\right\}\left(\frac{\omega^2 a_1^3}{3Gm_1}\right)^2 , \qquad (5\text{-}19)$$

where $\bar{\eta}_2$ denotes the surface value $(a = a_1)$ of Radau's homogeneous equation for $j = 2$, and η_2, η_4 (without bars) are surface values of logarithmic derivatives of the functions f_2, f_4 defined as particular solutions of the differential equations

$$a^2 f''_2 + 6D(af'_2 + f_2) - 6f_2 = \frac{2}{7}\{2af'_2(af'_2 + 9f_2) - 9Daf'_2(af'_2 + 2f_2)\}$$
$$+ \frac{3\omega^2}{\pi G\bar{\rho}}(1 - D)(af'_2 + f_2) \qquad (5\text{-}20)$$

and

$$a^2 f''_4 + 6D(af'_4 + f_4) - 20f_4$$
$$= \frac{18}{35}\{2af'_2(af'_2 + f_2) - 3D(3a^2 f'^2_2 + 6af_2 f'_2 + 7f_2^2)\} , \qquad (5\text{-}21)$$

subject to boundary conditions requiring that, at the origin $(a = 0)$

$$f'_2(0) = f'_4(0) = 0 , \qquad (5\text{-}22)$$

while on the surface $(a = a_1)$

$$2f_2(a_1) + a_1 f'_2(a_1) + \frac{5}{3}\left(\frac{\omega^2 a_1^3}{Gm_1}\right) = \frac{2}{3}\left(\frac{\omega^2 a_1^3}{Gm_1}\right)\{5f_2(a_1) + a_1 f'_2(a_1)\}$$
$$+ \frac{1}{7}\{2a_1^2 f'^2_2(a_1) + 6a_1 f_2(a_1) f'_2(a_1) + 12f_2^2(a_1)\} \qquad (5\text{-}23)$$

and

$$4f_4(a_1) + a_1 f'_4(a_1) = \frac{18}{35}\{a_1^2 f'^2_2(a_1) + 5a_1 f_2(a_1) f'_2(a_1) + 6f_2^2(a_1)\}. \qquad (5\text{-}24)$$

It may be noted that while the outer boundary condition for $f_2(a_1)$ is both nonlinear and nonhomogeneous, that for $f_4(a_1)$ is homogeneous and all quantities on both sides of equation (5-24) are of the same order of magnitude. It is, moreover, unnecessary to consider equations (5-20) and (5-21) as a simultaneous system; for, consistent with our scheme of approximation, it should be sufficient to solve first numerically the auxiliary boundary-value problem

$$\left.\begin{aligned} &a^2\bar{f}''_2 + 6D(a\bar{f}'_2 + \bar{f}_2) - 6\bar{f}_2 = 0 , \\ &\bar{f}'_2(0) = 0 , \quad 2\bar{f}_2(a_1) + a_1\bar{f}'_2(a_1) = -\frac{5}{3}\left(\frac{\omega^2 a_1^3}{Gm_1}\right) ; \end{aligned}\right\} \tag{5-25}$$

and by evaluating the right-hand sides of equations (5-20) - (5-21) and (5-23) - (5-24) in terms of its solution, to treat equations (5-20) and (5-21) as linear but nonhomogeneous.

The expansion of the external potential of a rotationally distorted configuration continues to be of the form (2-39), and its coefficients

$$k_j = \frac{4\pi F_j(a_1)}{(2j+1)Gm_1} \tag{5-26}$$

are again deducible from equations (1-20) and (2-38). Using appropriate values for $f_{2,4}(a_1)$ as given by (5-18) and (5-19), and the function c_2 as given by (5-10), we easily establish that, for the rotational problem,

$$k_2 = -\frac{3-\eta_2}{2+\eta_2}\left(\frac{\omega^2 a_1^3}{3Gm_1}\right) - \frac{40(4\bar{\eta}_2 + 3)}{7(\bar{\eta}_2 + 2)^3}\left(\frac{\omega^2 a_1^3}{3Gm_1}\right)^2 , \tag{5-27}$$

and

$$k_4 = \frac{90}{7(\bar{\eta}_2+2)}\left\{\frac{3+\bar{\eta}_2}{4+\eta_4} - \frac{\bar{\eta}_2}{2+\bar{\eta}_2}\right\}\left(\frac{\omega^2 a_1^3}{3Gm_1}\right)^2 , \tag{5-28}$$

where the surface value $\bar{\eta}_2$ of the logarithmic derivative of $\bar{f}_2$ can be deduced from the solution of (5-25).

III-6: LIMITING SOLUTIONS

In the preceding sections of this chapter we succeeded in developing a consistent second-order theory of the rotational or tidal distortion of self-gravitating compressible fluids of arbitrary internal structure. In two limiting cases of the density distribution—namely, for the homogeneous (Maclaurin) model (characterized by $D(a) = 1$ for $0 \leq a < a_1$) and the mass-point (Roche) model (consisting of a mass point at the center, and $D(a) = 0$ for $0 < a \leq a_1$)—the rotational as well as tidal problem have, however, long been solved in a closed form giving exact results. The aim of the present section will be to compare these exact solutions with the outcome of our own analysis particularized for $D = 0$ or 1 ; and to demonstrate that they agree indeed, as they should, to the expected order of accuracy.

In order to establish from our results of Section III-5 the form of a homogeneous configuration distorted by axial rotation to quantities of second order, let us begin by noting that equation (5-20) is satisfied for $D = 1$, with

$$f_2(a) = \text{constant} \tag{6-1}$$

and, therefore,

$$\eta_2(a) = 0 \tag{6-2}$$

to a second approximation; and the value of this constant follows from the boundary condition (5-23) as

$$f_2(a) = -\frac{5}{2}v - \frac{25}{14}v^2 + \ldots , \tag{6-3}$$

where we have abbreviated

$$v = \frac{2}{3}\left(\frac{\omega^2 a_1^3}{Gm_1}\right) = \frac{\omega^2}{2\pi G\rho} . \tag{6-4}$$

Similarly, equation (5-21) for f_4 is likewise satisfied by

$$f_4(a) = \text{constant}, \quad \eta_4(a) = 0 , \tag{6-5}$$

and the value of the constant follows from (5-24) as

$$f_4(a) = \frac{135}{112}v^2 + \ldots . \tag{6-6}$$

Lastly, by (1-26) and (6-3),

$$f_0(a) = -\frac{1}{5}f_2^2(a) = -\frac{5}{16}v^2 + \ldots \tag{6-7}$$

to the same order of accuracy. Therefore, to the second-order scheme of approximation,

$$\left.\begin{aligned} f_0 &= -\frac{5}{16}v^2 + \ldots , \\ f_2 &= -\frac{5}{4}v - \frac{25}{14}v^2 + \ldots , \\ f_4 &= +\frac{135}{112}v^2 + \ldots . \end{aligned}\right\} \tag{6-8}$$

Now if, consistent with (5-1),

$$r' = a\{1 + f_0 + f_2P_2(\nu) + f_4P_4(\nu) + \ldots\} , \tag{6-9}$$

and as, at the pole $(\nu = 1)$ $P_2 = P_4 = 1$ while, at the equator $(\nu = 0)$ $P_2 = -\frac{1}{2}$ and $P_4 = \frac{3}{8}$, the equatorial and polar semi-axes a' and c' of our rotational spheroid becomes

$$a' = a\{1 + \frac{5}{8}v + \frac{925}{896}v^2 + \ldots \} , \tag{6-10}$$

$$c' = a\{1 - \frac{5}{4}v - \frac{25}{28}v^2 + \dots\} , \tag{6-11}$$

leading to an eccentricity

$$e^2 = \frac{a'^2 - c'^2}{a'^2} = \frac{15}{4}v - \frac{1}{7}(\frac{15}{4}v)^2 + \dots . \tag{6-12}$$

An inversion of this equation yields, in turn,

$$v = \frac{4}{15}e^2 + \frac{4}{105}e^4 + \dots , \tag{6-13}$$

in agreement with an expansion of the exact closed expression*

$$v = \frac{3-2e^2}{e^3}\sqrt{1-e^2}\ \sin^{-1}e - 3(\frac{1}{e^2} - 1) \tag{6-14}$$

which, as

$$\sqrt{1-e^2}\ \sin^{-1}e = e\left\{1 - \sum_{n=1}^{\infty} \frac{4^{n-1}[(n-1)!]^2}{(2n-1)!\,(2n+1)} e^{2n}\right\}, \tag{6-15}$$

can be shown to be expansible as

$$v = \frac{4}{15}e^2 + \frac{4}{105}e^4 - \frac{32}{3465}e^8 + \dots . \tag{6-16}$$

We notice that, as the term of the order of e^6 is missing in this expansion of the right-hand side of equation (6-14), our second-order theory for a homogeneous configuration attains, in fact, third-order accuracy.

Let us next turn our attention to the other limiting model of the range of configurations considered in this book—namely, the mass-point (Roche) model, in which the total mass of a configuration is supposed to be condensed at its center, surrounded by an infinitesimally thin envelope of ignorable attraction. If so, however, then the interior potential U arising from this envelope vanishes identically, while the exterior potential V reduces to the first term of its expansion on the right-hand side of equation (1-24) of Chapter II.

As a result, the total potential Ψ of such a configuration reduces then to

$$\Psi = V_0 + V'_{rot} + V'_t ; \tag{6-17}$$

and if we insert for the individual quantities on the right from (1-24) ,

* For its derivation cf., e.g. J. H. Jeans, Problems of Astronomy and Stellar Dynamics, Cambridge Univ. Press, 1919, p. 38.

(5-1) and (5-14) of Chapter II in which (to free ourselves from any approximation) we replace a by r', the total potential of a configuration built up according to the Roche model, distorted by rotation and tides, assumes the exact closed form

$$\Psi = G\frac{m_1}{r'} + \frac{Gm_2}{\sqrt{R^2 - 2r'R\lambda + r'^2}} - \frac{1}{2}\omega^2 r'^2(1-\nu^2) , \tag{6-18}$$

where $m_{1,2}$ denote the masses of the distorted and disturbing body; R, the separation of their centers; ω^2, the angular velocity of rotation; G, the gravitation constant; and the direction cosines

$$\lambda = \cos\phi' \sin\theta' \quad \text{and} \quad \nu = \cos\theta . \tag{6-19}$$

Equation (6-18) cleared of fractions and radicals is of eighth degree in r'. It can, however, be solved conveniently for it by successive approximations. The details of such a process are rather outside the scope of this section*; but the result discloses that, correctly to quantities of second order**,

$$\begin{aligned} \frac{r'-a'}{a'} = {} & \left(\frac{a'}{R}\right)^3\{q P_2(\lambda) + w(1-\nu^2)\} \\ & + \left(\frac{a'}{R}\right)^3\{q P_3(\lambda)\} + \left(\frac{a'}{R}\right)^5 \{q P_4(\lambda)\} \\ & + \left(\frac{a'}{R}\right)^6 \{q P_5(\lambda) + 3[q P_2(\lambda) + w(1-\nu^2)]^2\} \\ & + \left(\frac{a'}{R}\right)^7 \{q P_6(\lambda) + 7q[q P_2(\lambda) + w(1-\nu^2)]P_3(\lambda)\} \\ & + \left(\frac{a'}{R}\right)^8 \{q P_7(\lambda) + 8q[q P_2(\lambda) + w(1-\nu^2)]P_4(\lambda) \\ & \qquad + 4q^2[P_3(\lambda)]\} + \ldots , \end{aligned} \tag{6-20}$$

where we have abbreviated

$$q = \frac{m_2}{m_1} , \quad w = \frac{\omega^2 R^3}{2Gm_1} , \tag{6-21}$$

and

---

* Cf., Z. Kopal, Jodrell Bank Annals, 1, 37, 1954; or his Close Binary Systems (London and New York, 1959), section III-2.

** In the references just given the present writer constructed the requisite expansion for r' consistently to the quantities of third order.

$$\frac{R}{a'} = \frac{R\Psi}{Gm_1} - \frac{m_2}{m_1} \;. \qquad (6\text{-}22)$$

Now consider first the case of a purely rotational distortion ($q = 0$), in which the foregoing equation (6-20) reduces to

$$r' = a'\{1 + (\frac{a'}{R})^3 w(1 - \nu^2) + 3(\frac{a'}{R})^6 w^2(1 - \nu^2)^2 + \dots\} \qquad (6\text{-}23)$$

On the other hand, if we note that

$$\left.\begin{aligned} 2P_2(\nu) &= 2 - 3(1 - \nu^2) \;, \\ 8P_4(\nu) &= 8 - 40(1 - \nu^2) + 35(1 - \nu^2)^2 \;, \end{aligned}\right\} \qquad (6\text{-}24)$$

our equation (5-1) can be likewise rewritten in terms of the sectorial harmonics as

$$r' = a'\{1 - (\frac{3}{2}f_2 - \frac{3}{2}f_2^2 + 5f_4)(1 - \nu^2) + \frac{35}{8}f_4(1 - \nu^2)^2 + \dots\}, \qquad (6\text{-}25)$$

where we have abbreviated

$$a' = a(1 + f_0 + f_2 + f_4) \;. \qquad (6\text{-}26)$$

Moreover, if $D = 0$ for $a > 0$, equations (5-20) to (5-24) together with (1-26) reveal—by the same method as in the preceding homogeneous case—that, for the Roche model,

$$f_0 = -\frac{1}{45}\left(\frac{\omega^2 a^3}{Gm_1}\right)^2 + \dots, \qquad (6\text{-}27)$$

$$f_2 = -\frac{1}{3}\left(\frac{\omega^2 a^3}{Gm_1}\right) - \frac{8}{63}\left(\frac{\omega^2 a^3}{Gm_1}\right)^2 + \dots, \qquad (6\text{-}28)$$

$$f_4 = +\frac{6}{35}\left(\frac{\omega^2 a^3}{Gm_1}\right)^2 + \dots \;. \qquad (6\text{-}29)$$

In consequence,

$$\left.\begin{aligned} \frac{3}{2}f_2 - \frac{3}{2}f_2^2 + 5f_4 &= -\frac{1}{2}\left(\frac{\omega^2 a^3}{Gm_1}\right) + \frac{1}{2}\left(\frac{\omega^2 a^3}{Gm_1}\right)^2 + \dots \\ &= -\frac{1}{2}\left(\frac{\omega^2 a'^3}{Gm_1}\right) + \dots = -(\frac{a'}{R})^3 w \end{aligned}\right\} \qquad (6\text{-}30)$$

by (6-25) and (6-21). Since, moreover

$$\frac{35}{8}f_4 = \frac{3}{4}\left(\frac{\omega^2 a'^3}{Gm_1}\right) = 3(\frac{a'}{R})^6 w^2 , \qquad (6\text{-}31)$$

the expressions on the right-hand sides of equations (6-23) and (6-25) are indeed seen to be identical—quod erat demonstrandum.

As the last example of a solution to be given in this section, let us consider the explicit form of a mass-point model distorted tidally to quantities of second order. If $D = 0$ and, accordingly $\overline{\eta}_j = j+1$ throughout the interior, Radau's equations (2-26) with $T_j(a)$ as given by (2-29)-(2-35) will, for $j = 1(1)7$, assume the explicit form

$$a\eta'_1 + \eta_1(\eta_1 + 1) - 2 = 40 , \tag{6-32}$$

$$a\eta'_2 + \eta_2(\eta_2 - 1) - 6 = \frac{144}{7}\frac{m_2}{m_1}\left(\frac{a}{R}\right)^3 + \frac{3200}{21}\frac{m_2}{m_1}\left(\frac{a}{R}\right)^5, \tag{6-33}$$

$$a\eta'_3 + \eta_3(\eta_3 - 1) - 12 = 56\frac{m_2}{m_1}\left(\frac{a}{R}\right)^3 , \tag{6-34}$$

$$a\eta'_4 + \eta_4(\eta_4 - 1) - 20 = \frac{108}{7}\frac{m_2}{m_1}\left(\frac{a}{R}\right)^3 + \frac{8352}{77}\frac{m_2}{m_1}\left(\frac{a}{R}\right)^5, \tag{6-35}$$

$$a\eta'_5 + \eta_5(\eta_5 - 1) - 30 = 40\frac{m_2}{m_1}\left(\frac{a}{R}\right) , \tag{6-36}$$

$$a\eta'_6 + \eta_6(\eta_6 - 1) - 42 = \frac{2480}{77}\frac{m_2}{m_1}\left(\frac{a}{R}\right) , \tag{6-37}$$

$$a\eta'_7 + \eta_7(\eta_7 - 1) - 56 = 0 , \tag{6-38}$$

and their approximate solutions become

$$\eta_1(a) = 7 + \ldots , \tag{6-39}$$

$$\eta_2(a) = 3 + \frac{18}{7}\frac{m_2}{m_1}\left(\frac{a}{R}\right)^3 + \frac{320}{21}\frac{m_2}{m_1}\left(\frac{a}{R}\right)^5 + \ldots , \tag{6-40}$$

$$\eta_3(a) = 4 + \frac{28}{5}\frac{m_2}{m_1}\left(\frac{a}{R}\right)^3 + \ldots , \tag{6-41}$$

$$\eta_4(a) = 5 + \frac{54}{35}\frac{m_2}{m_1}\left(\frac{a}{R}\right) + \frac{696}{33}\frac{m_2}{m_1}\left(\frac{a}{R}\right)^3 + \ldots , \tag{6-42}$$

$$\eta_5(a) = 6 + \frac{10}{3}\frac{m_2}{m_1}\left(\frac{a}{R}\right) + \ldots , \tag{6-43}$$

$$\eta_6(a) = 7 + \frac{1240}{231}\frac{m_2}{m_1}(\frac{a}{R}) + \ldots \ , \tag{6-44}$$

$$\eta_7(a) = 8 + \ldots \ . \tag{6-45}$$

As a result, the corresponding amplitudes $f_j(a)$ of distortion are eventually found from equations (2-17) to (2-24) to be

$$f_1(a) = \frac{9}{5}\left(\frac{m_2}{m_1}\right)^2 (\frac{a}{R})^7 \tag{6-46}$$

$$f_2(a) = \frac{m_2}{m_1}(\frac{a}{R})^3 + \frac{6}{7}\left(\frac{m_2}{m_1}\right)^2 (\frac{a}{R})^6 + \frac{64}{21}\left(\frac{m_2}{m_1}\right)^2 (\frac{a}{R})^8 \tag{6-47}$$

$$f_3(a) = \frac{m_2}{m_1}(\frac{a}{R})^4 + \frac{28}{15}\left(\frac{m_2}{m_1}\right)^2 (\frac{a}{R})^7 \tag{6-48}$$

$$f_4(a) = \frac{m_2}{m_1}(\frac{a}{R})^5 + \frac{54}{35}\left(\frac{m_2}{m_1}\right)^2 (\frac{a}{R})^6 + \frac{232}{77}\left(\frac{m_2}{m_1}\right)^2 (\frac{a}{R})^8 \tag{6-49}$$

$$f_5(a) = \frac{m_2}{m_1}(\frac{a}{R})^6 + \frac{10}{3}\left(\frac{m_2}{m_1}\right)^2 (\frac{a}{R})^7 \tag{6-50}$$

$$f_6(a) = \frac{m_2}{m_1}(\frac{a}{R})^7 + \frac{1240}{231}\left(\frac{m_2}{m_1}\right)^2 (\frac{a}{R})^8 \tag{6-51}$$

$$f_7(a) = \frac{m_2}{m_1}(\frac{a}{R})^8 \tag{6-52}$$

In comparing this outcome with the equation (6-20) obtained by an expansion of the closed Roche potential (6-18), we are entitled (as the tides do not influence the volume of a distorted configuration to the first order in small quantities) to ignore the difference between a and a'. If, moreover, the squares and cross-products of the individual $P_j(\lambda)$'s on the right-hand side of (6-20) are linearized by means of the equations (1-4)-(1-7), the coefficients of the individual harmonics of tidal origin are again found to be in complete agreement with the foregoing equations (6-45)-(6-52)— Q. E. D.

III-7: EFFECTS OF DISTORTION ON INTERNAL STRUCTURE

Throughout all preceding developments in this volume our sole concern has so far been to establish explicit expressions for the form of equipotential surfaces of self-gravitating compressible fluids distorted by arbitrary forces, and for the gravitational potential of such configurations. Any disturbing force will, however, not only distort the shape and influence the potential; it will also affect the distribution of density and pressure in the interior of such a configuration; and while these effects have not so far made any explicit appearance in our analysis*, it may be of general interest to investigate them to the same order of accuracy as we have done with the external form and potential. The aim of the present section will be to provide such an investigation.

As could be expected, the problems of the form and internal structure will be found to be closely interrelated; and, in particular, a knowledge of the potential will open a direct way for the complete solution of the effects of distortion on the entire internal structure as well. In fact, once the potential $U + V$ arising from the mass of the distorted configuration and represented by a sum of the equations (1-19) and (1-20) has been determined, the (disturbed) internal density distribution follows readily from the Poisson equation

$$\nabla^2 (U + V) = -4\pi G\rho \; ; \tag{7-1}$$

and the corresponding pressure P from the relation

$$P \equiv P(\rho) \tag{7-2}$$

representing the equation of state**.

In order to set forth the requisite relations in more explicit form, let us introduce the non-dimensional variables

$$\left.\begin{aligned} r &= a_1\xi \, , \\ \rho &= \rho_c\theta \, , \\ P &= P_c\pi = (4\pi G\rho_c^2 a_1^2)\pi \, , \\ U + V &= (4\pi G\rho_c a_1^2)\chi \, , \end{aligned}\right\} \tag{7-3}$$

where a_1 denotes, as before, the mean external radius of our configuration; ρ_c, P_c, its central density and pressure; and G, the constant of gravitation. If so, the Poisson equation (7-1) rewritten in terms of the foregoing non-dimensional variables assumes readily the form

* It may be recalled that the function $\rho(a)$ introduced in Section II-1 refers to the internal density distribution of our configuration in its initial spherical form (which the configuration would possess if the cause of distortion were removed).

** H. Poincaré (Leçons sur les Hypothèses Cosmogoniques, Paris 1913, p. 32) proved that the conservation of momentum alone is bound to guarantee the existence of some pressure-density relation of the form (7-2).

$$\frac{1}{\xi^2}\left\{\frac{\partial}{\partial\xi}\left(\xi^2\frac{\partial\chi}{\partial\xi}\right)+\frac{\partial}{\partial\ell}\left[(1-\ell)\frac{\partial\chi}{\partial\ell}\right]\right\} = -\theta \ , \tag{7-4}$$

where ℓ denotes the cosine of the angle between an arbitrary radius-vector and the axis of symmetry of the disturbing force (i.e., z in the case of rotational distortion, and x in the problem of the tides).

Let, moreover, the disturbing force (whether due to axial rotation, or the tidal action of an external mass) be characterized by a small parameter ϵ responsible for the distortion, and let the functions $\theta(\xi,\ell;\epsilon)$, $\pi(\xi,\ell;\epsilon)$, and $\chi(\xi,\ell;\epsilon)$ be regarded as analytic in ϵ at $\epsilon = 0$. If so, it is legitimate to postulate the existence of asymptotic expansions of the form

$$\theta = \theta_0(\xi) + \epsilon\theta_1(\xi,\ell) + \epsilon^2\theta_2(\xi,\ell) + \dots \ , \tag{7-5}$$

$$\pi = \pi_0(\xi) + \epsilon\pi_1(\xi,\ell) + \epsilon^2\pi_2(\xi,\ell) + \dots \ , \tag{7-6}$$

$$\chi = \chi_0(\xi) + \epsilon\chi_1(\xi,\ell) + \epsilon^2\chi_2(\xi,\ell) + \dots \ , \tag{7-7}$$

where the functions $\theta_0(\xi)$, $\pi_0(\xi)$, and $\chi_0(\xi)$ describe the equilibrium structure of the respective configuration in its initial (undistorted) state.

Inserting (7-5) with (7-7) in (7-4) and equating terms factored by equal powers of ϵ , we find that the constituent functions θ_j of the expansion (7-5) for normalized internal density distribution should be given by the equations

$$\frac{1}{\xi^2}\left\{\frac{\partial}{\partial\xi}\left(\xi^2\frac{\partial\chi_0}{\partial\xi}\right)\right\} = -\theta_0 \ , \tag{7-8}$$

$$\frac{1}{\xi^2}\left\{\frac{\partial}{\partial\xi}\left(\xi^2\frac{\partial\chi_1}{\partial\xi}\right)+\frac{\partial}{\partial\ell}\left[(1-\ell^2)\frac{\partial\chi_1}{\partial\ell}\right]\right\} = -\theta_1 \ , \tag{7-9}$$

$$\frac{1}{\xi^2}\left\{\frac{\partial}{\partial\xi}\left(\xi^2\frac{\partial\chi_2}{\partial\xi}\right)+\frac{\partial}{\partial\ell}\left[(1-\ell^2)\frac{\partial\chi_2}{\partial\ell}\right]\right\} = -\theta_2 \ , \tag{7-10}$$

etc., where the terms χ_j constituting the disturbing potential have already been established in section III-1 for an arbitrary field of force, and can be written down almost at once after appropriate normalization.

Moreover, once the explicit form of the expansion (7-5) has thus been obtained, the corresponding pressure distribution can be deduced from equation (7-2) which in terms of our normalized variables assumes the form

$$\pi(\xi,\ell;\epsilon) \equiv \pi\{\theta(\xi,\ell;\epsilon)\} \ . \tag{7-11}$$

If the case $\epsilon = 0$ corresponds to an equilibrium configuration (i.e., a sphere), the functions on both sides of the foregoing relation must be analytic at $\epsilon = 0$. If so, however, we may resort to a Taylor expansion

$$\pi = \pi(\theta_0) + \epsilon\left(\frac{d\pi}{d\epsilon}\right)_0 + \frac{\epsilon^2}{2}\left(\frac{d^2\pi}{d\epsilon^2}\right) + \dots , \tag{7-12}$$

where

$$\left(\frac{d\pi}{d\epsilon}\right)_0 = \left(\frac{d\pi}{d\theta}\frac{d\theta}{d\epsilon}\right)_0 = \theta_1\frac{d\pi_0}{d\theta_0} , \tag{7-13}$$

$$\left(\frac{d^2\pi}{d\epsilon^2}\right)_0 = \theta_1{}^2\frac{d^2\pi_0}{d\theta_0{}^2} + 2\theta_2\frac{d\pi_0}{d\theta_0} , \tag{7-14}$$

etc., —so that, accordingly,

$$\pi = \pi_0 + \epsilon\left\{\theta_1\frac{d\pi_0}{d\theta}\right\} + \frac{\epsilon^2}{2}\left\{\theta_1{}^2\frac{d^2\pi_0}{d\theta_0{}^2} + 2\theta_2\frac{d\pi_0}{d\theta_0}\right\} + \dots \tag{7-15}$$

A comparison of this series with the expansion on the right-hand side of equation (7-6) then readily reveals that

$$\pi_1 = \theta_2\frac{d\pi_0}{d\theta_0} , \tag{7-16}$$

$$\pi_2 = \theta_2\frac{d\pi_0}{d\theta_0} + \frac{\theta_1{}^2}{2}\frac{d^2\pi_0}{d\theta_0{}^2} ; \tag{7-17}$$

or, if the functions describing the equilibrium structure of our configuration are known, π_1 and π_2 may be more conveniently described as

$$\pi_1 = \theta_1\left\{\frac{\dfrac{d\pi_0}{d\xi}}{\dfrac{d\theta_0}{d\xi}}\right\} \tag{7-18}$$

and

$$\pi_2 = \theta_2\left\{\frac{\dfrac{d\pi_0}{d\xi}}{\dfrac{d\theta_0}{d\xi}}\right\} + \frac{\theta_1{}^2}{2}\left\{\frac{\dfrac{d^2\pi_0}{d\xi^2}\dfrac{d\theta_0}{d\xi} - \dfrac{d\pi_0}{d\xi}\dfrac{d^2\theta_0}{d\xi^2}}{\left(\dfrac{d\theta_0}{d\xi}\right)^2}\right\}, \tag{7-19}$$

respectively.

All developments given so far in this section have been completely general and applicable to the case of either rotational or tidal distortion. In order to demonstrate their more explicit form on a simple example, let us assume that our configuration is distorted by axial rotation with constant angular velocity about the z-axis, in which case $\ell \equiv \nu$. If so, we have learned earlier in sections III-1 and 5 of this chapter that the potential arising from the mass of the rotating configuration can be expressed in the form of an expansion equivalent to

$$\chi(\xi, \nu; \epsilon) = \sum_{j=0}^{4} \left\{ \xi^j E_j + \frac{F_j}{\xi^{j+1}} \frac{P_j(\nu)}{2j+1} \right\}, \tag{7-20}$$

where, to the second order in small quantities, the only nonvanishing (normalized) terms are known to be,

$$E_0(\xi) = \int_{\xi}^{\xi_1} \theta_0(\xi) \frac{\partial}{\partial \xi} \{\xi^2 (\tfrac{1}{2} - \tfrac{1}{10} f_2{}^2)\} d\xi , \tag{7-21}$$

$$E_2(\xi) = \int_{\xi}^{\xi_1} \theta_0(\xi) \frac{\partial}{\partial \xi} \{f_2 - \tfrac{1}{7} f_2{}^2\} d\xi , \tag{7-22}$$

$$E_4(\xi) = \int_{\xi}^{\xi_1} \theta_0(\xi) \frac{\partial}{\partial \xi} \{\tfrac{1}{\xi^2} (f_4 - \tfrac{27}{35} f_2{}^2)\} d\xi ; \tag{7-23}$$

and

$$F_0(\xi) = \int_0^{\xi} \theta_0(\xi) \xi^2 d\xi , \tag{7-24}$$

$$F_2(\xi) = \int_0^{\xi} \theta_0(\xi) \frac{\partial}{\partial \xi} \{\xi^5 (f_2 + \tfrac{4}{7} f_2{}^2)\} d\xi , \tag{7-25}$$

$$F_4(\xi) = \int_0^{\xi} \theta_0(\xi) \frac{\partial}{\partial \xi} \{\xi^7 (f_4 + \tfrac{54}{35} f_2{}^2)\} d\xi . \tag{7-26}$$

If, moreover, the individual functions $\chi_j(\xi, \nu)$ on the right-hand side of equation (7-7) are, accordingly, developed into a sum of products of separate functions of ξ and ν as

$$\chi_j(\xi, \nu) = \sum_{k=0}^{2j} \chi_{j,k}(\xi) P_k(\nu) , \tag{7-27}$$

the desired functions $\theta_j(\xi, \nu)$ for $j = 1, 2$ constituting the density expansion (7-5) can be defined, more explicitly, by the equations

$$\theta_1(\xi, \nu) = \frac{1}{\xi^2} \left\{ 6\chi_{1,2} - \frac{\partial}{\partial \xi} \left(\xi^2 \frac{\partial \chi_{1,2}}{\partial \xi} \right) \right\} P_2(\nu) \tag{7-28}$$

and

$$\theta_2(\xi,\nu) = \frac{1}{\xi^2}\left\{ \qquad -\frac{\partial}{\partial\xi}\left(\xi^2\,\frac{\partial\chi_{2,0}}{\partial\xi}\right)\right\}$$

$$+\frac{1}{\xi^2}\left\{ 6\chi_{2,2} - \frac{\partial}{\partial\xi}\left(\xi^2\,\frac{\partial\chi_{2,2}}{\partial\xi}\right)\right\} P_2(\nu) \tag{7-29}$$

$$+\frac{1}{\xi^2}\left\{ 20\chi_{2,4} - \frac{\partial}{\partial\xi}\left(\xi^2\,\frac{\partial\chi_{2,4}}{\partial\xi}\right)\right\} P_4(\nu) \; ,$$

respectively,. where

$$\left.\begin{aligned} 5\epsilon\chi_{1,2}(\xi) &= \xi^2\int_\xi^{\xi_1}\theta_0(\xi)\frac{\partial f_2}{\partial\xi}d\xi + \frac{1}{\xi^3}\int_0^\xi \theta_0(\xi)\frac{\partial}{\partial\xi}(\xi^5 f_2)d\xi \\ &= 5\left\{\frac{f_2}{\xi}\int_0^\xi \theta_0(\xi)\xi^2 d\xi - \frac{c_{0,2}\xi^2}{4\pi G\rho_c}\right\} \end{aligned}\right\} \tag{7-30}$$

by virtue of Clairaut's equation (1-32) of Chapter II satisfied by f_2 ; and, similarly,

$$\epsilon^2\chi_{2,0}(\xi) = -\frac{1}{10}\int_\xi^{\xi_1}\theta_0(\xi)\frac{\partial}{\partial\xi}(\xi^2 f_2{}^2)d\xi \; , \tag{7-31}$$

while

$$\epsilon^2\chi_{2,2}(\xi) = \frac{1}{\xi}\left\{R_2(\xi) - \frac{\xi}{7}\,\frac{\partial f_2{}^2}{\partial\xi}\right\} \tag{7-32}$$

and

$$\epsilon^2\chi_{2,4}(\xi) = \frac{f_4}{\xi}\int_0^\xi \theta_0(\xi)\xi^2 d\xi + \frac{1}{\xi}\left\{R_4(\xi) - \frac{9\xi}{35}\,\frac{\partial f_2{}^2}{\partial\xi}\right\} \; , \tag{7-33}$$

where the functions $R_{2,4}(\xi)$ continue to be given by equation (1-43), and the $f_j(\xi)$'s can likewise be regarded as known from our previous work.

With the aid of these relations it is easy to establish (by differentiation) that

$$\frac{1}{\xi^2}\left\{6\chi_{1,2} - \frac{\partial}{\partial\xi}(\xi^2\,\frac{\partial\chi_{1,2}}{\partial\xi})\right\} = -(\xi\theta'_0)f_2 \tag{7-34}$$

and

$$\begin{aligned} &\frac{1}{\xi^2}\left\{ \qquad -\frac{\partial}{\partial\xi}(\xi^2\,\frac{\partial\chi_{2,0}}{\partial\xi})\right\} \\ &\qquad = -\frac{\theta_0}{5}\{\eta_2{}^2 + 6(1-D)(\eta_2+1) + (\eta_2+1)\left(\frac{\xi\theta'_0}{\theta_0}\right) + 3\}f_2{}^2 \; , \end{aligned} \tag{7-35}$$

$$\frac{1}{\xi^2}\left\{6\chi_{2,2} - \frac{\partial}{\partial \xi}(\xi^2 \frac{\partial \chi_{2,2}}{\partial \xi})\right\}$$
$$= -\frac{2\theta_0}{7}\left\{\eta_2{}^2 + 6(1-D)(\eta_2+1) + (\eta_2+2)\left(\frac{\xi\theta'_0}{\theta_0}\right)\right\}f_2{}^2 \, , \qquad (7\text{-}36)$$

$$\frac{1}{\xi^2}\left\{20\chi_{2,4} - \frac{\partial}{\partial \xi}(\xi^2 \frac{\partial \chi_{2,4}}{\partial \xi})\right\} = -(\xi\theta'_0)f_4$$
$$-\frac{18}{35}\theta_0\left\{\eta_2{}^2 + 6(1-D)(\eta_2+1) + (\eta_2+2)\left(\frac{\xi\theta'_0}{\theta_0}\right) - 7\right\}f_2{}^2, \qquad (7\text{-}37)$$

where, it may be remembered,

$$\frac{\xi\theta'_0}{\theta_0} = a\frac{D'}{D} - 3(1-D) \; . \qquad (7\text{-}38)$$

Once the equations (7-34)-(7-37) have been inserted in (7-28) and (7-29), the coefficients $\epsilon\theta_1$ and $\epsilon^2\theta_2$ in the expansion (7-5) of the density become known functions of η_2 , D , f_2 and f_4 and can be evaluated from the results of the preceding sections.

In conclusion of the present section two points should be particularly noted. First, all the developments we outlined hold good for any arbitrary initial structure of the distorted star; they neither define it, nor are they dependent on any of its particular features. Secondly, all our developments contain no explicit reference to any equations of motion or state; and, in particular, the latter developments are not restricted to configurations rotating like rigid bodies. The equations of motion, or any particular form of a possibly variable angular velocity of rotation should influence the explicit form of the potential expansion (7-7) through the constants $c_{i,j}$ in Clairaut's equation; but they are all implicit in f_2 or f_4 and our present formulation contains no direct reference to them.

III-8: MOMENTS OF INERTIA

In conclusion of our discussion of the second-order effects on self-gravitating fluid configurations produced by rotation or tides, the last task still confronting us is to derive explicit expressions for the principal moments of inertia of distorted configurations about their axes of symmetry. In order to do so, let us identify these axes with our xyz-rectangular system defined, as before, in such a way that

$$\left.\begin{aligned} x &= r' \cos\phi' \sin\theta' \, , \\ y &= r' \sin\phi' \sin\theta' \, , \\ z &= r' \cos\theta \, ; \end{aligned}\right\} \qquad (8\text{-}1)$$

and let, furthermore, the symbols A, B, C denote the moments of inertia of our configurations about the axes x, y, z respectively. If so, it follows by definition that

$$A = \int (y^2 + z^2)dm' \ , \tag{8-2}$$

$$B = \int (x^2 + z^2)dm' \ , \tag{8-3}$$

$$C = \int (x^2 + y^2)dm' \ , \tag{8-4}$$

where

$$\int \equiv \int_0^{r_1}\int_0^{\pi}\int_0^{2\pi} \tag{8-5}$$

and the mass element dm' continues to be given by

$$dm' = \rho r'^2 \sin\theta' \, d\theta' \, d\phi' \ , \tag{8-6}$$

in accordance with equation (1-4) of Chapter II.

In order to evaluate the foregoing integrals, let us resort again to Clairaut's artifice (1-10) of Chapter II, which enables us to rewrite (8-2)-(8-4) alternatively as

$$A = \frac{1}{5}\int_0^{a_1} \rho \frac{\partial}{\partial a}\left\{\int_0^{\pi}\int_0^{2\pi} r'^5(\sin^2\theta' \sin^2\phi' + \cos^2\theta')\sin\theta' d\theta' d\phi'\right\} da \ , \tag{8-7}$$

$$B = \frac{1}{5}\int_0^{a_1} \rho \frac{\partial}{\partial a}\left\{\int_0^{\pi}\int_0^{2\pi} r'^5(\sin^2\theta' \cos^2\phi' + \cos^2\theta')\sin\theta' d\theta' d\phi'\right\} da \ , \tag{8-8}$$

and

$$C = \frac{1}{5}\int_0^{a_1} \rho \frac{\partial}{\partial a}\left\{\int_0^{\pi}\int_0^{2\pi} r'^5 \sin^3\theta' d\theta' d\phi'\right\} da \tag{8-9}$$

respectively, where

$$r' = a\{1 + \sum f_j P_j\} \tag{8-10}$$

continues to be given by (1-1) or (5-1).

In order to progress further, let us consider first the case of rotational distortion, and to this end identify the z-axis with the axis of rotation of our configuration (while xy- coincides with its equatorial plane). If so, then obviously $P_j \equiv P_j(\cos\theta')$; and a term-by-term integration of the expressions in curly brackets on the right-hand sides of equations (8-7)-(8-9) reveals that, for a configuration of constant mass, the principal moments A', B', C' of inertia assume the more explicit forms

$$A' = B' = \frac{2}{5}\pi\int_0^{a_1}\rho\frac{\partial}{\partial a}\left\{a^5\left[\frac{4}{3}+\frac{2}{3}f_2+\frac{12}{7}f_2^{\,2}+\ldots\right]\right\}da \tag{8-11}$$

and

$$C' = \frac{2}{5}\pi\int_0^{a_1}\rho\frac{\partial}{\partial a}\left\{a^5\left[\frac{4}{3}-\frac{4}{3}f_2+\frac{4}{7}f_2^{\,2}+\ldots\right]\right\}da\ , \tag{8-12}$$

correctly to quantities of second order.

In consequence

$$A' - C' = \frac{4}{5}\pi\int_0^{a_1}\rho\frac{\partial}{\partial a}\left\{a^5\left[f_2+\frac{4}{7}f_2^{\,2}+\ldots\right]\right\}da\ ; \tag{8-13}$$

and if, moreover,

$$I = \frac{2}{5}\pi\int_0^{a_1}\rho\frac{\partial}{\partial a}\left\{\frac{4}{3}a^5\right\}da = \frac{8}{3}\pi\int_0^{a_1}\rho a^4 da \tag{8-14}$$

denotes the moment of inertia of our configuration about its center of mass, it follows from the foregoing results that

$$A' + B' + C' - 3I = \frac{8}{5}\pi\int_0^{a_1}\rho\frac{\partial}{\partial a}(a^5 f_2^{\,2})da\ , \tag{8-15}$$

where the function $f_2(a)$ continues to be given by equations (5-20) and (5-22)-(5-23), or their simplified version (5-25). The reader may note that, within the scheme of our approximation, all three moments of inertia involve solely f_2 and are independent of f_4 ; moreover, the quantity $A' + B' + C' - 3I$ turns out to be one of second order.

Turning now to the effects of <u>tidal distortion</u>, let us identify our x-axis with the semi-major axis of the prolate configuration (coinciding in direction with the line joining the centers of the distorted and disturbing body), so that now $P_j \equiv P_j(\cos\phi'\sin\theta')$ in (8-10). On raising this latter expansion to the fifth power and retaining terms consistently to the quantities of second order, a term-by-term integration of (8-7)-(8-9) reveals that the principal moments A", B", C" of inertia of a tidally-distorted configuration of constant mass assume the more explicit forms

$$\begin{aligned} A'' = \frac{2}{5}\pi\int_0^{a_1}\rho\frac{\partial}{\partial a}\Bigg\{a^5\Bigg[&\frac{4}{3}+\frac{5}{2}f_1-\frac{4}{3}f_2-\frac{5}{3}f_3+\frac{65}{96}f_5-\frac{13}{32}f_7 \\ &+\frac{4}{7}f_2^{\,2}+\frac{4}{9}f_3^{\,2}+\frac{25}{12}f_2f_3-\frac{32}{21}f_2f_4\Bigg]\Bigg\}da \end{aligned} \tag{8-16}$$

and

$$B'' = C'' = \frac{2}{5}\pi\int_0^{a_1}\rho\frac{\partial}{\partial a}\left\{a^5\left[\frac{4}{3}+\frac{15}{4}f_1+\frac{2}{3}f_2-\frac{5}{12}f_3+\frac{55}{192}f_5 -\frac{3}{16}f_7+\frac{12}{7}f_2^2+\frac{76}{63}f_3^2+\frac{95}{24}f_2f_3 +\frac{16}{21}f_2f_4\right]\right\}da\,, \tag{8-17}$$

so that

$$C'' - A'' = \frac{2}{5}\pi\int_0^{a_1}\rho\frac{\partial}{\partial a}\left\{a^5\left[\frac{5}{4}f_1+2f_2+\frac{5}{4}f_3-\frac{25}{64}f_5+\frac{7}{32}f_7 +\frac{8}{7}f_2^2+\frac{16}{21}f_3^2+\frac{15}{8}f_2f_3+\frac{16}{7}f_2f_4\right]\right\}da \tag{8-18}$$

and

$$A'' + B'' + C'' - 3I = 4\pi\int_0^{a_1}\rho\frac{\partial}{\partial a}\left\{a^5\left[f_1-\frac{1}{4}f_3+\frac{1}{8}f_5-\frac{5}{64}f_7 +\frac{2}{5}f_2^2+\frac{2}{7}f_3^2+f_2f_3\right]\right\}da\,, \tag{8-19}$$

where the individual f_j's have already been formulated, to the requisite degree of accuracy, in the preceding sections III-2 and 4. The reader may, moreover, note that—unlike (8-15)—the right-hand side of the foregoing equation (8-19) proves to be a quantity of first order, due to the presence of the coefficient f_3 of the third harmonic tidal distortion; all other quantities in the square brackets being again of second order.

IV

INTERACTION PHENOMENA

In the preceding two chapters of this monograph, a theory of purely rotational or tidal distortion of self-gravitating fluid bodies has been systematically developed to terms of second order in superficial distortion, and explicit expressions set up for the gravitational potential of such a configuration. If, however, the rotating body is subject also to a tidal action of an external mass—as are the components of close double stars, or the Earth attracted by the Sun and the Moon—both forces will be simultaneously operative, and will affect jointly the resultant distortion. This interaction between rotation and tides has, however, been so far left out of consideration in our work on grounds of simplicity. Yet such a neglect is not really legitimate if we wish to develop a self-consistent second-order theory; for, as we have seen in section II-5, the leading terms due to both rotation and tides are of first order; and the nonlinear nature of our problem is bound to make them interact through their products. No second-order theory of the distortion of compressible fluids by rotation and tides can, therefore, be regarded as complete until these cross-terms have been duly taken into account; and their investigation constitutes a task to which we shall address ourselves in the present chapter.

This task will prove to be very much more complicated than any problem treated in the preceding chapters, which serve merely as necessary preliminaries to this end. In particular, the number and complexity of terms which must be simultaneously considered is such as to make it very easy to lose sight of the essential features of the whole problem; and the way through this unhealthy mathematical swamp abounds with so many false tracks that a single step in the wrong direction may cause the whole analysis to bog down in fathomless complexities. Having eventually found our way we propose to take our reader to the desired results along a closely marked trail and ignore the pitfalls or difficulties which had to be avoided or circumvented; anyone who may deviate from the main line of our argument can easily discover them at his own risk.

IV-1: INTERACTION BETWEEN ROTATION AND TIDES: GEOMETRICAL PRELIMINARIES

In order to investigate the problem of interaction between the polar flattening produced by a given centrifugal force and tides raised on a rotating configuration by an arbitrary external field, let us adopt a rectangular frame of reference XYZ , with origin at the center of mass of the distorted configuration, whose axes are fixed in space; the Z-axis coinciding with that of rotation. As in our previous work, the direction cosines of an arbitrary radius-vector r in this system will be given by

$$\left.\begin{aligned} \lambda &= \cos\phi \sin\theta , \\ \mu &= \sin\phi \sin\theta , \\ \nu &= \cos\theta , \end{aligned}\right\} \quad (1-1)$$

while

$$\left.\begin{aligned} \lambda' &= \cos\phi' \sin\theta' \\ \mu' &= \sin\phi' \sin\theta' \\ \nu' &= \cos\theta' \end{aligned}\right\} \quad (1-2)$$

will denote the position of an arbitrary point of the distorted configuration. If, moreover, γ denotes, as before, the angle between the radius-vector r and an arbitrary internal point, we continue to have

$$\left.\begin{aligned} \cos\gamma &= \lambda\lambda' + \mu\mu' + \nu\nu' \\ &= \cos\theta\cos\theta' + \sin\theta\sin\theta'\cos(\phi - \phi') \end{aligned}\right\} \quad (1-3)$$

in accordance with (1-6) of Chapter II.

Let, furthermore, the tide-generating body (be it the Sun, the Moon, or a stellar companion) revolve in an X"Y"-plane inclined to that of XY (i.e., the equator of the rotating configuration by an angle i , and Ω denote the angle of intersection between these two planes; u being the position angle of the disturbing body, in its orbital plane, measured from Ω *. If so, the direction cosines λ'', μ'', ν'' of the line joining the centers of the two bodies in the XYZ-frame of references will (in agreement with equations 5-16 of Chapter II) be given by

$$\left.\begin{aligned} \lambda'' &= \cos u \cos\theta - \sin u \sin\theta \cos i &= \cos p \sin q , \\ \mu'' &= \cos u \sin\theta + \sin u \cos\theta \cos i &= \sin p \sin q , \\ \nu'' &= \sin u \sin i &= \cos q , \end{aligned}\right\} \quad (1-4)$$

* In common astronomical terminology the angles i, Ω, u are known as the obliquity of the ecliptic, the longitude of the ascending node, and true anomaly of the disturbing body (measured from Ω).

where the auxiliary angles

$$\left.\begin{aligned} p &= \Omega + \tan^{-1}(\cos i \ \tan u) , \\ q &= \cos^{-1}(\sin i \ \sin u) , \end{aligned}\right\} \quad (1-5)$$

Moreover, the angles Θ , Θ' between the radii-vectors r, r' and the line joining the centers of the two bodies are then obviously given by

$$\left.\begin{aligned} \cos \Theta &= \lambda\lambda'' + \mu\mu'' + \nu\nu'' \\ &= \cos q \cos \theta + \sin q \sin \theta \cos(p - \phi) \end{aligned}\right\} \quad (1-6)$$

and

$$\left.\begin{aligned} \cos \Theta' &= \lambda'\lambda'' + \mu'\mu'' + \nu'\nu'' \\ &= \cos q \cos \theta' + \sin q \sin \theta' \cos(p - \phi'), \end{aligned}\right\} \quad (1-7)$$

respectively.

Now in section II-5 of this monograph we pointed out that whereas, to the terms of first order in small quantities, the axial rotation gives rise to a single spherical harmonic distortion varying as $P_2(\nu)$, the tidal distortion invokes three distinct harmonics of the form $P_j(\cos \Theta)$, $j = 2, 3, 4$. Therefore, a development of the radius-vector consistent to quantities of second order is bound to contain cross-terms of the form

$$P_2(\nu) \, P_j(\cos \Theta) , \quad j = 2, 3, 4 , \tag{A}$$

which have not been taken into account in equation (1-1) of Chapter III.

Suppose that we now do so, and include the products of the form (A) in the expression for r' used to evaluate the U_j's and V_j's, as defined by equations (1-13) and (1-23), constituting our potential expansions (1-7) and (1-19) in Chapter II. Doing so, however, we find it necessary to consider—besides (1-16) of Chapter II-- also more generalized orthogonality conditions for the <u>triple</u> products of general spherical harmonics referred to arbitrarily oriented space axes—i.e., to evaluate the integrals of the products $P_2(\nu') \, P_j(\cos \Theta) \, P_n(\cos \gamma)$ over the whole sphere in terms of the direction cosines λ, μ, ν and λ'', μ'', ν'' .

This evaluation becomes, needless to say, rather difficult, as no general theorems analogous to (1-16) of Chapter II are known to facilitate our task. By the addition theorem for Legendre polynomials $P_n(\cos \gamma)$ continues to be expansible in a series of the form

$$P_n(\cos \gamma) = P_n(\nu) \, P_n(\nu') + 2 \sum_{i=1}^{n} \frac{(n-i)!}{(n+i)!} P_n^i(\nu) \, T_n^i(\nu') , \tag{1-8}$$

where we have abbreviated,

$$T_n^i(\nu') = \cos i(\phi - \phi')\, P_n^i(\nu') \; ; \tag{1-9}$$

and, similarly,

$$P_j(\cos \Theta) = P_j(\nu')\, P_j(\nu'') + 2\sum_{i=1}^{j} \frac{(j-i)!}{(j+i)!} P_j^i(\nu'')\, T_j^i(\nu'), \tag{1-10}$$

where

$$T_j^i(\nu') = \cos i(p - \phi')\, P_j^i(\nu') \; . \tag{1-11}$$

Moreover, by use of the algebraic identity

$$\begin{aligned} \sin^2\theta'\, T_j^i(\nu') &= 2\left\{\frac{i^2 + j(j+1) - 1}{(2j-1)(2j+3)}\right\} T_j^i(\nu') \\ &- \frac{(i+j)(i+j-1)}{(2j+1)(2j-1)} T_{j-2}^i(\nu') \\ &- \frac{(j-i+1)(j-i+2)}{(2j+1)(2j+3)} T_{j+2}^i(\nu') \end{aligned} \tag{1-12}$$

it is possible to reduce the triple products $P_2(\nu')\, P_j(\cos \Theta)\, P_n(\cos \gamma)$ into double products of general spherical harmonics to which the orthogonality condition (1-16) of Chapter II should be applicable. Doing so and abbreviating

$$\begin{aligned} &\int_0^{\pi}\int_0^{2\pi} P_j(\cos \Theta)\, P_n(\cos \gamma)\, P_2^2(\cos \theta')\, \sin \theta' d\theta' d\phi' \\ &= \frac{4\pi}{2n+1} \mathbb{P}_n^{(j)}(\cos \Theta \,; \nu, \nu'') \; , \end{aligned} \tag{1-13}$$

we find—after a considerable amount of algebra—that for $0 \leq j \leq 4$ and $0 \leq n \leq 7$ the non-vanishing $\mathbb{P}_j^{(i)}$'s assume the explicit forms

$$\mathbf{P}^{(0)}_{2} = P^2_2(\nu) - 2 \ , \tag{1-14}$$

$$\mathbf{P}^{(1)}_{1} = + \frac{12}{5} P_1(\cos\Theta) - \frac{6}{5}\nu\nu'' \ , \tag{1-15}$$

$$\mathbf{P}^{(1)}_{3} = P^2_2(\nu)\, P_1(\cos\Theta) - \frac{12}{5} P_1(\cos\Theta) + \frac{6}{5}\nu\nu'' \ ; \tag{1-16}$$

$$\mathbf{P}^{(2)}_{0} = - \frac{2}{5} P_2(\nu'') \ , \tag{1-17}$$

$$\mathbf{P}^{(2)}_{2} = - \frac{2}{7} P^2_2(\nu) + \frac{18}{7} P_2(\cos\Theta) - \frac{18}{7}\nu\nu'' P_1(\cos\Theta) + \frac{4}{7} P_2(\nu'') + \frac{6}{7} \ , \tag{1-18}$$

$$\mathbf{P}^{(2)}_{4} = P^2_2(\nu)\, P_2(\cos\Theta) + \frac{2}{7} P^2_2(\nu) - \frac{18}{7} P_2(\cos\Theta) + \frac{18}{7}\nu\nu'' P_1(\cos\Theta) - \frac{6}{35} P_2(\nu'') - \frac{6}{7} \ ; \tag{1-19}$$

$$\mathbf{P}^{(3)}_{1} = - \frac{9}{35}(5\nu''^2 - 1)\, P_1(\cos\Theta) + \frac{18}{35}\nu\nu'' \ , \tag{1-20}$$

$$\mathbf{P}^{(3)}_{3} = - \frac{2}{3} P^2_2(\nu)\, P_1(\cos\Theta) + \frac{8}{3} P_3(\cos\Theta) - \frac{10}{3}\nu\nu'' P_2(\cos\Theta) + \frac{2}{5}(5\nu''^2 + 4)\, P_1(\cos\Theta) - \frac{22}{15}\nu\nu'' \ , \tag{1-21}$$

$$\mathbf{P}^{(3)}_{5} = P^2_2(\nu)\, P_3(\cos\Theta) + \frac{2}{3} P^2_2(\nu)\, P_1(\cos\Theta) - \frac{8}{3} P_3(\cos\Theta) + \frac{10}{3}\nu\nu'' P_2(\cos\Theta) - \frac{1}{7}(5\nu''^2 + 13)\, P_1(\cos\Theta) + \frac{20}{21}\nu\nu'' \ ; \tag{1-22}$$

$$\mathbf{P}^{(4)}_{2} = \frac{1}{21} P^2_2(\nu) - \frac{5}{21}(7\nu''^2 - 1)\, P_2(\cos\Theta) + \frac{10}{7}\nu\nu'' P_1(\cos\Theta) - \frac{20}{63} P_2(\nu'') - \frac{16}{63} \tag{1-23}$$

$$\mathbf{P}^{(4)}_{4} = - \frac{10}{11} P^2_2(\nu)\, P_2(\cos\Theta) - \frac{20}{77} P^2_2(\nu) + \frac{30}{11} P_4(\cos\Theta) - \frac{42}{11}\nu\nu'' P_3(\cos\Theta) + \frac{30}{77}(7\nu''^2 + 6)\, P_2(\cos\Theta) - \frac{306}{77}\nu\nu'' P_1(\cos\Theta) + \frac{40}{77} P_2(\nu'') + \frac{74}{77} \tag{1-24}$$

$$\mathbf{P}^{(4)}_{6} = P^2_2(\nu)\, P_4(\cos\Theta) + \frac{10}{11} P^2_2(\nu)\, P_2(\cos\Theta) + \frac{7}{33} P^2_2(\nu) - \frac{30}{11} P_4(\cos\Theta) + \frac{42}{11}\nu\nu'' P_3(\cos\Theta) - \frac{5}{33}(7\nu''^2 + 17)\, P_2(\cos\Theta) + \frac{28}{11}\nu\nu'' P_1(\cos\Theta) - \frac{20}{99} P_2(\nu'') - \frac{70}{99} \ ; \tag{1-25}$$

suggesting the existence of a general relation of the form

$$\mathbf{P}^{(j)}_{j-2} + \mathbf{P}^{(j)}_{j} + \mathbf{P}^{(j)}_{j+2} = P_2^2(\nu)\, P_j(\cos\Theta) \ . \qquad (1\text{-}26)$$

The emergence, on the right-hand sides of the foregoing equations (1-18)-(1-25), of terms varying as

$$P_1(\nu)\, P_j(\cos\Theta) \qquad (B)$$

leads us to consider further orthogonality conditions for triple products of spherical harmonics of the form $P_1(\nu')\, P_j(\cos\Theta')\, P_n(\cos\gamma)$. These can again be reduced to double products by observing that, for $j > 0$,

$$(2j+1)\nu\, T^i_j(\nu) = (i+j)\, T^i_{j-1}(\nu) + (j-i+1)\, T^i_{j+1}(\nu) \ . \qquad (1\text{-}27)$$

Making use of this identity we find it again possible to express integrals of the form

$$\left.\begin{aligned} &\int_0^{\pi}\int_0^{2\pi} P_j(\cos\Theta')\, P_n(\cos\gamma)\, \sin\theta' \cos\theta' d\theta' d\phi' = \\ &= \frac{4\pi}{2n+1}\, \mathbf{Q}^{(j)}_n(\cos\Theta\,;\nu,\nu'') \ , \quad 0 \le j \le 3 \ , \\ &\qquad\qquad\qquad\qquad\qquad\qquad 0 \le n \le 7 \ , \end{aligned}\right\} \qquad (1\text{-}28)$$

in terms of those represented by equation (1-16) of Chapter II; and the outcome reveals the non-vanishing $\mathbf{P}^{(j)}$'s to become

$$\mathbf{Q}^{(0)}_0 = \nu \ ; \qquad (1\text{-}29)$$

$$\mathbf{Q}^{(1)}_0 = \qquad + \frac{1}{3}\nu'' \ , \qquad (1\text{-}30)$$

$$\mathbf{Q}^{(1)}_2 = \nu P_1(\cos\Theta) - \frac{1}{3}\nu'' \ ; \qquad (1\text{-}31)$$

$$\mathbf{Q}^{(2)}_1 = \qquad + \frac{3}{5}\nu'' P_1(\cos\Theta) - \frac{1}{5}\nu \ , \qquad (1\text{-}32)$$

$$\mathbf{Q}^{(2)}_3 = \nu P_2(\cos\Theta) - \frac{3}{5}\nu'' P_1(\cos\Theta) + \frac{1}{5}\nu \ ; \qquad (1\text{-}33)$$

$$\mathbf{Q}^{(3)}_2 = \qquad + \frac{5}{7}\nu'' P_2(\cos\Theta) - \frac{3}{7}\nu P_1(\cos\Theta) + \frac{1}{7}\nu'' \ , \qquad (1\text{-}34)$$

$$\mathbf{Q}^{(3)}_4 = \nu P_3(\cos\Theta) - \frac{5}{7}\nu'' P_2(\cos\Theta) + \frac{3}{7}\nu P_1(\cos\Theta) - \frac{1}{7}\nu'' \ , \qquad (1\text{-}35)$$

so that, by analogy with (1-26),

$$\mathbb{Q}_{j-1}^{(j)} + \mathbb{Q}_{j+1}^{(j)} = \nu P_j(\cos\Theta) \ . \qquad (1-36)$$

The foregoing expressions (1-29)-(1-35) for the $\mathbb{Q}$'s contain no harmonic terms of types other than (A) or (B); in consequence, the full-dress expression for the radius-vector of a tidally distorted configuration rotating about an axis inclined to the orbital plane should, to the second order in superficial distortion, be of the form

$$r' = a\left\{1 + \sum_{i=0}^{7} f_i P_i(\cos\Theta') + \sum_{i=0}^{3} h_i P_1(\nu') P_i(\cos\Theta') + \sum_{i=0}^{4} \hbar_i P_2^2(\nu') P_i(\cos\Theta') + \hbar\!\!\!/_0 P_4^4(\nu')\right\} \qquad (1-37)$$

generalizing equation (1-1) of Chapter III of the purely rotational or tidal problem.

When we inspect the structure of the foregoing equation (1-37), we may recall from previous chapters of this monograph that, to the first order in small quantities, the tidal distortion has given rise to three distinct harmonics, with coefficients f_i $(i = 2, 3, 4)$, while the rotational distortion invoked a single term corresponding to $\hbar_0$. A retention of second-order terms in Chapter III augmented the number of purely tidal harmonics from 3 to 7, and that of the rotational terms from 1 to 2. We now find that an interaction between rotation and tides will, in general, give rise to 7 entirely new terms of mixed origin—i.e., three h_i's $(i = 1, 2, 3)$ and four $\hbar_i$'s $(i = 1, 2, 3, 4)$—as well as a new purely rotational term with the coefficient h_0. Therefore, if an expression of the form of equation (1-11) of Chapter II for the radius-vector r' of a distorted equipotential was found to consist of four distinct tesseral harmonics within the scheme of first-order approximation, its extension to terms of second order has now increased their number from 4 to 17, consisting of 13 rotational terms and 14 partial tides which sweep around the distorted configuration in different periods and phases.

It should, however, be clearly stated that all the f's and h's which we shall proceed to construct in this chapter arise solely from <u>interaction</u> between rotation and tides—and are, therefore, <u>additive</u> to terms arising from pure rotation or tides and investigated already in the preceding Chapter III. In particular, all seven purely tidal f's of section III-4 will superpose upon the interaction f's to be investigated in the present chapter and factoring the same surface harmonic; the same will be true of the rotational functions f_2 and f_4 of section III-5, and the new functions $\hbar_0$ and $\hbar\!\!\!/_0$ introduced on the right-hand side of equation (1-37).

In compounding the latter, care should merely be taken to note that whereas the right-hand side of equation (5-1) of Chapter III constitutes an expansion in terms of the zonal harmonics of increasing order, the sectorial harmonics are used in (1-37). However, as

$$\left.\begin{aligned} P_2^2 &= 2(1 - P_2) , \\ P_4^4 &= 8(7 - 10P_2 + 3P_4) , \end{aligned}\right\} \qquad (1-38)$$

and, therefore,

$$\left.\begin{aligned} P_2 &= 1 - \frac{1}{2} P_2^2 , \\ P_4 &= 1 - \frac{5}{3} P_2^2 + \frac{1}{24} P_4^4 , \end{aligned}\right\} \qquad (1-39)$$

it follows that, in a complete expansion for r' of the form (1-37), $\hbar_0$ should be augmented by $-(\frac{1}{2} f_2 + \frac{5}{3} f_4)_{rot}$, and $\hbar_0$ by $\frac{1}{24} (f_4)_{rot}$. Similarly, the coefficient f_0 of the harmonic of zero order should be augmented—apart from the purely tidal term f_0 as given by equation (1-26) of Chapter III—also by $(f_2 + f_4 - \frac{1}{5} f_2^2)_{rot}$, where the "rotational" f_j's can be found in section III-5. All the "interaction" f's and h's introduced in (1-37) through the orthogonality conditions (1-18)-(1-25) are, however, new; and the aim of the subsequent sections of this chapter will be to deduce their explicit forms for rotating configurations of arbitrary internal structure, and subject to a tidal pull from arbitrary direction.

IV-2: POTENTIAL EXPANSIONS

With the foregoing geometrical preliminaries now complete, we are in a position to proceed with the formulation of the mixed potential in the same way as we have done in earlier chapters of this monograph. Let, in accordance with equations (1-7) and (1-19) of Chapter II, the internal and external potential at any point be expansible as

$$U = \sum_{n=0}^{\infty} r^n U_n , \qquad (2-1)$$

$$V = \sum_{n=0}^{\infty} \frac{V_n}{r^{n+1}} , \qquad (2-2)$$

where the contributions U_n and V_n arising from the interaction between rotation and tides (and, therefore, additive to those due to pure rotation or tides established in Chapter III) are given by the equations

$$(2n+1)U_n = 4\pi G \sum_{i,j,k} P_j^i(\nu)\, P_k(\cos\,\Theta) \int_a^{a_1} \rho \frac{\partial}{\partial a} \left\{ a^{2-n} \Phi_{j,k}^{(i)n} \right\} da\,, \quad (2\text{-}3)$$

$$(2n+1)V_n = 4\pi G \sum_{i,j,k} P_j^i(\nu)\, P_k(\cos\,\Theta) \int_0^{a} \rho \frac{\partial}{\partial a} \left\{ a^{n+3} \Phi_{j,k}^{(i)n} \right\} da\,, \quad (2\text{-}4)$$

where

$$\Phi_{0,n}^{(0)n} = F_n\,, \qquad 1 \le n \le 7\,; \quad (2\text{-}5)$$

$$\Phi_{1,n-1}^{(0)n} = H_{n-1}\,, \qquad 1 \le n \le 4\,; \quad (2\text{-}6)$$

$$\Phi_{2,n-2}^{(2)n} = \widetilde{H}_{n-2}\,, \qquad 2 \le n \le 6\,; \quad (2\text{-}7)$$

$$\Phi_{0,n-2}^{(0)n} = -\left\{ \frac{2n-3}{2n-1}\, \nu''\, H_{n-1} + \frac{6(n-1)}{2n-1}\, \widetilde{H}_{n-2} \right\}, \quad 2 \le n \le 6\,; \quad (2\text{-}8)$$

$$\Phi_{1,n-3}^{(0)n} = \frac{2n-5}{2n-1} \left\{ H_{n-1} + 6\nu''\, \widetilde{H}_{n-2} \right\}, \qquad 3 \le n \le 6\,; \quad (2\text{-}9)$$

$$\Phi_{2,n-4}^{(2)n} = 2 \left\{ \frac{2n-7}{2n-1} \right\} \widetilde{H}_{n-2}\,, \qquad 4 \le n \le 6\,; \quad (2\text{-}10)$$

and

$$\left.\begin{aligned} \Phi_{0,0}^{(0)4} &= -\frac{1}{7}\nu''\, H_3 - \frac{3}{35}(3\nu''^2 + 9)\, \widetilde{H}_2\,, \\ \Phi_{0,1}^{(0)5} &\doteq -\frac{1}{7}(5\nu''^2 + 13)\, \widetilde{H}_3\,, \\ \Phi_{0,2}^{(0)6} &= -\frac{5}{33}(7\nu''^2 + 17)\, \widetilde{H}_4\,; \end{aligned}\right\} \quad (2\text{-}11)$$

$$\Phi_{1,0}^{(0)5} = -\frac{20}{21}\nu''\, \widetilde{H}_3\,, \quad \Phi_{1,1}^{(0)6} = \frac{28}{11}\nu''\, \widetilde{H}_4\,; \quad (2\text{-}12)$$

$$\Phi_{0,0}^{(0)6} = -\frac{10}{33}(\nu''^2 + 2)\, \widetilde{H}_4\,, \quad \Phi_{2,0}^{(2)6} = \frac{7}{33}\, \widetilde{H}_4\,; \quad (2\text{-}13)$$

$$F_0 = f_0 + \frac{1}{3} \qquad - \frac{1}{5}(3\nu''^2 - 1)\hbar_2 \,, \tag{2-14}$$

$$F_1 = f_1 + \frac{3}{5}h_2\nu'' + \frac{12}{5}\hbar_1 - \frac{9}{35}(5\nu''^2 - 1)\hbar_3 \,, \tag{2-15}$$

$$F_2 = f_2 + \frac{5}{7}h_3\nu'' + \frac{18}{7}\hbar_2 - \frac{5}{21}(7\nu''^2 - 1)\hbar_4 \,, \tag{2-16}$$

$$F_3 = f_3 + \frac{8}{3}\hbar_3 \,, \tag{2-17}$$

$$F_4 = f_4 + \frac{30}{11}\hbar_4 \,, \tag{2-18}$$

$$F_5 = f_5 \,, \tag{2-19}$$

$$F_6 = f_6 \,, \tag{2-20}$$

$$F_7 = f_7 \,; \tag{2-21}$$

$$H_0 = h_0 - \frac{1}{5}h_2 - \frac{6}{5}\hbar_1\nu'' + \frac{18}{35}\hbar_3\nu'' \,, \tag{2-22}$$

$$H_1 = h_1 - \frac{3}{7}\hbar_3 - \frac{18}{7}h_2\nu'' + \frac{10}{7}\hbar_4\nu'' \,, \tag{2-23}$$

$$H_2 = h_2 - \frac{10}{3}\hbar_3\nu'' \,, \tag{2-24}$$

$$H_3 = h_3 - \frac{42}{11}\hbar_4\nu'' \,; \tag{2-25}$$

$$\widetilde{H}_0 = \hbar_0 - \frac{2}{7}\hbar_2 + \frac{1}{21}\hbar_4 \,, \tag{2-26}$$

$$\widetilde{H}_1 = \hbar_1 - \frac{2}{3}\hbar_3 \,, \tag{2-27}$$

$$\widetilde{H}_2 = \hbar_2 - \frac{10}{11}\hbar_4 \,, \tag{2-28}$$

$$\widetilde{H}_3 = \hbar_3 \,, \tag{2-29}$$

$$\widetilde{H}_4 = \hbar_4 \,; \tag{2-30}$$

the functions f_j , h_j , $\hbar_j$ being the same as defined on the right-hand side of equation (1-37) for the radius-vector. Their linear combinations F_j , H_j and $\widetilde{H}_j$ for values of j greater than those listed above are zero within the scheme of second-order approximation.

Having progressed thus far, we find now ourselves in a position to construct the Clairaut equation (1-42) of Chapter III, which expresses the equality of the total potential over free surface $(r = r')$ of a rotating-fluid configuration distorted by tidal forces acting from an arbitrary direction, correctly to quantities of second order. Needless to stress, its explicit form turns out to be rather involved: for whereas 16 terms were sufficient to set it up to first-order approximation (i.e., four terms for the rotational distortion, and another four for each of the three partial tides), a consistent second-order theory with interaction between rotation and tides duly taken into account requires a retention of not less than 302 distinct terms whose sum constitutes the total potential.

The explicit form of this potential is, of course, much too long to be fully reproduced in this place, and to do so is also unnecessary; for our actual task is merely to ensure the constancy of this potential over any level surface by equating the coefficients of all individual harmonics of the form $P_j^i(\nu)P_k(\cos\Theta)$ to zero; this should provide the requisite number of equations for complete specification of all functions f_j, h_j and $\hbar_j$ involved on the right-hand side of equation (1-37). After a rather considerable amount of algebra we thus find the constancy of the total potential to require that the functions F_j, H_j and $\widetilde{H}_j$ should satisfy the following integral equations

$$F_j\int_0^a \rho a^2\,da - \frac{1}{(2j+1)a^j}\int_0^a \rho\frac{\partial}{\partial a}(a^{j+2}F_j)\,da - \frac{a^{j+1}}{2j+1}\int_0^{a_1}\rho\frac{\partial}{\partial a}(a^{2-j}F_j)\,da = a\left\{a\frac{\partial}{\partial a}(\mathscr{F}_j)\right\}\int_0^a \rho a^2\,da \tag{2-31}$$

for $1 \leq j \leq 7$,

$$H_j\int_0^a \rho a^2\,da - \frac{1}{(2j+3)a^{j+1}}\int_0^a \rho\frac{\partial}{\partial a}(a^{j+4}H_j)\,da - \frac{a^{j+2}}{2j+3}\int_a^{a_1}\rho\frac{\partial}{\partial a}(a^{1-j}H_j)\,da = \left\{a\frac{\partial}{\partial a}(\mathscr{G}_j)\right\}\nu''\int_0^a \rho a^2\,da \tag{2-32}$$

for $0 \leq j \leq 3$, and

$$\widetilde{H}_j \int_0^a \rho a^2 \, da - \frac{1}{(2j+5)a^{j+2}} \int_0^a \rho \frac{\partial}{\partial a}(a^{j+5}\widetilde{H}_j) da$$

$$- \frac{a^{j+3}}{2j+5} \int_a^{a_1} \rho \frac{\partial}{\partial a}(a^{-j}\widetilde{H}_j) da \tag{2-33}$$

$$= \left\{ a \frac{\partial}{\partial a}(\mathscr{H}_j) \right\} \int_0^a \rho a^2 \, da$$

for $0 \leq j \leq 4$, where the (non-vanishing) functions $\mathscr{F}_j$, $\mathscr{G}_j$, $\mathscr{H}_j$ are found to assume the explicit forms

$$\mathscr{F}_1 = -\frac{9}{35}(5\nu''^2 - 1) f_3 g_2 \ , \tag{2-34}$$

$$\mathscr{F}_2 = \frac{18}{7} f_2 g_2 - \frac{5}{21}(7\nu''^2 - 1) f_4 g_2 \ , \tag{2-35}$$

$$\mathscr{F}_3 = \frac{8}{3} f_3 g_2 \ , \tag{2-36}$$

$$\mathscr{F}_4 = \frac{30}{11} f_4 g_2 \ ; \tag{2-37}$$

$$\mathscr{G}_0 = +\frac{18}{35} f_3 g_2 \ , \tag{2-38}$$

$$\mathscr{G}_1 = -\frac{18}{7} f_2 g_2 + \frac{10}{7} f_4 g_2 \ , \tag{2-39}$$

$$\mathscr{G}_2 = -\frac{10}{3} f_3 g_2 \ , \tag{2-40}$$

$$\mathscr{G}_3 = -\frac{42}{11} f_4 g_2 \ ; \tag{2-41}$$

$$\mathscr{H}_0 = -\frac{2}{7} f_2 g_2 + \frac{1}{21} f_4 g_2 \ , \tag{2-42}$$

$$\mathscr{H}_1 = -\frac{2}{3} f_3 g_2 \ , \tag{2-43}$$

$$\mathscr{H}_2 = f_2 g_2 - \frac{10}{11} f_4 g_2 \ , \tag{2-44}$$

$$\mathscr{H}_3 = f_3 g_2 \ , \tag{2-45}$$

$$\mathscr{H}_4 = f_4 g_2 \ . \tag{2-46}$$

In these equations the quantities f_j $(j = 2, 3, 4)$ stand for the first--order terms of the coefficients of the respective tidal harmonic distortion, and g_2, for that of the second-harmonic rotational distortion—all of which are known to us from first-order theory treated in Chapter II. Noting, moreover, that, in accordance with equation (2-41) of Chapter III,

$$a\frac{\partial}{\partial a}(f_j g_2) = (\eta_j + \eta_2) f_j g_2 \quad , \quad j = 2, 3, 4 \quad , \qquad (2\text{-}47)$$

where the η_j's denote (as before) the logarithmic derivatives of the respective functions satisfying equations (1-40)-(1-41) of Chapter II, we see that all quantities occurring on the right-hand sides of equations (2-31)-(2-32), and (2-33) can be regarded as known, and the equations themselves solved for F_j, H_j and $\widetilde{H}_j$ in terms of derivatives of the products $f_j g_2$ representing interaction between the first--order effects of the rotation and tides.

IV-3: EXTERNAL FORM: INTERACTION TERMS

In the foregoing section we succeeded in formulating the specific form of second-order Clairaut's equations (2-31)-(2-33) defining, in principle, the external form as well as potential of a fluid configuration distorted by rotation and tides. Owing to the fact that the effects of these forces are interlocked in second-order terms, the equations (2-31)-(2-33) as they stand do not, however, define the radial functions f_j, h_j and $\hbar_j$ explicitly, but rather certain linear combinations F_j, H_j and $\widetilde{H}_j$ of them as defined by equations (2-14)-(2-30). A continued use of the auxiliary functions F_j, H_j, $\widetilde{H}_j$ will, moreover, simplify all our subsequent algebra to such an extent that a transition from them to f_j, h_j and $\hbar_j$ should be postponed with advantage till the final stage of our analysis.

In order to proceed with it let us multiply equations (2-31)-(2-33) by a^j, a^{j+1}, a^{j+2}, differentiate with respect to a, and divide by a^{j-1}, a^j, a^{j+1}, respectively: we find that

$$\left\{ j F_j + a\frac{\partial F_j}{\partial a} \right\} \int_0^a \rho\, a^2\, da - a^{j+1} \int_a^{a_1} \rho \frac{\partial}{\partial a}(a^{2-j} F_j) da$$

$$= a^2 \left\{ \frac{\partial^2 \mathscr{F}_j}{\partial a^2} + a(j+1)\frac{\partial \mathscr{F}_j}{\partial a} \right\} \int_0^a \rho\, a^2 da \qquad (3\text{-}1)$$

$$+ \rho\, a^4 \frac{\partial}{\partial a}(\mathscr{F}_j) \quad ,$$

$$\left\{(j+1)H_j + a\frac{\partial H_j}{\partial a}\right\}\int_0^a \rho a^2\, da - a^{j+2}\int_a^{a_1} \rho\frac{\partial}{\partial a}(a^{1-j}H_j)da$$

$$= \left\{a^2\frac{\partial^2\mathscr{G}_j}{\partial a^2} + a(j+2)\frac{\partial\mathscr{G}_j}{\partial a}\right\}\int_0^a \rho a^2\, da \tag{3-2}$$

$$+ \nu''\rho a^4\frac{\partial}{\partial a}(\mathscr{G}_j) ,$$

and

$$\left\{(j+2)H_j + a\frac{\partial H_j}{\partial a}\right\}\int_0^a \rho a^2\, da - a^{j+3}\int_a^{a_1} \rho\frac{\partial}{\partial a}(a^{-j}H_j)da$$

$$= \left\{a^2\frac{\partial^2\mathscr{H}_j}{\partial a^2} + a(j+3)\frac{\partial\mathscr{H}_j}{\partial a}\right\}\int_0^a \rho a^2\, da + \rho a^4\frac{\partial}{\partial a}(\mathscr{H}_j) , \tag{3-3}$$

for $0 \le j \le 4$.

The functions $\mathscr{F}_j$, $\mathscr{G}_j$ and $\mathscr{H}_j$ continue to be given by equations (2-34)-(2-46) of the preceding section. If advantage is taken of (2-47) as well as of the fact that the η_j-functions satisfy Radau's first-order differential equation (1-40) of Chapter II, we easily establish that

j	$a^2\frac{\partial^2\mathscr{F}_j}{\partial a^2} + a(j+1)\frac{\partial\mathscr{F}_j}{\partial a}$
1	$-\frac{9}{35}(5\nu''^2 - 1)\{2\eta_2\eta_3 + 2(\eta_2+\eta_3) + 18 - 6D(\eta_2+\eta_3+2)\}f_3g_2$
2	$-\frac{5}{21}(7\nu''^2-1)\{2\eta_2\eta_4 + 3(\eta_2+\eta_4) + 26 - 6D(\eta_2+\eta_4+2)\}f_4g_2$ $+\frac{36}{7}\{\eta_2^2+3\eta_2 + 6 - 6D(\eta_2+1)\}f_2g_2$,
3	$\frac{8}{3}\{2\eta_2\eta_3 + 4(\eta_2+\eta_3) + 18 - 6D(\eta_2+\eta_3+2)\}f_3g_2$,
4	$\frac{30}{11}\{2\eta_2\eta_4 + 5(\eta_2+\eta_4) + 26 - 6D(\eta_2+\eta_4+2)\}f_4g_2$;

j	$a^2\frac{\partial^2\mathscr{G}_j}{\partial a^2} + a(j+2)\frac{\partial\mathscr{G}_j}{\partial a}$
0	$\frac{18}{35}\{2\eta_2\eta_3 + 2(\eta_2+\eta_3) + 18 - 6D(\eta_2+\eta_3+2)\}f_3g_2$;
1	$\frac{10}{7}\{2\eta_2\eta_4 + 3(\eta_2+\eta_4) + 26 - 6D(\eta_2+\eta_4+2)\}f_4g_2$ $- \frac{36}{7}\{\eta_2^2 + 3\eta_2 + 6 - 6D(\eta_2+1)\}f_2g_2$,
2	$- \frac{10}{3}\{2\eta_2\eta_3 + 4(\eta_2+\eta_3) + 18 - 6D(\eta_2+\eta_3+2)\}f_3g_2$,
3	$- \frac{42}{11}\{2\eta_2\eta_4 + 5(\eta_2+\eta_4) + 26 - 6D(\eta_2+\eta_4+2)\}f_4g_2$;

j	$a^2\frac{\partial^2\mathscr{H}_j}{\partial a^2} + a(j+3)\frac{\partial\mathscr{H}_j}{\partial a}$
0	$- \frac{4}{7}\{\eta_2^2 + 3\eta_2 + 6 - 6D(\eta_2+1)\}f_2g_2$ $+ \frac{1}{21}\{2\eta_2\eta_4 + 3(\eta_2+\eta_4) + 26 - 6D(\eta_2+\eta_4+2)\}f_4g_2$,
1	$- \frac{2}{3}\{2\eta_2\eta_3 + 4(\eta_2+\eta_3) + 18 - 6D(\eta_2+\eta_3+2)\}f_3g_2$,
2	$2\{\eta_2^2 + 5\eta_2 + 6 - 6D(\eta_2+1)\}f_2g_2$ $- \frac{10}{11}\{2\eta_2\eta_4 + 5(\eta_2+\eta_4) + 26 - 6D(\eta_2+\eta_4+2)\}f_4g_2$,
3	$\{2\eta_2\eta_3 + 6(\eta_2+\eta_3) + 18 - 6D(\eta_2+\eta_3+2)\}f_3g_2$,
4	$\{2\eta_2\eta_4 + 7(\eta_2+\eta_4) + 26 - 6D(\eta_2+\eta_4+2)\}f_4g_2$;

where $D \equiv \rho/\bar{\rho}$ in accordance with our previous practice.

In order to evaluate the effects of interaction between rotation and tides on the external radius of our configuration, it is sufficient to set, in equations (2-1)-(2-3), $a = a_1$ —a step which annihilates the second integrals on their left-hand sides, as well as all terms multiplied by ρ or D. If, furthermore, we revert now to the original functions f_j, h_j and $\mathcal{K}_j$ by an inversion of the equations (2-14)-(2-30) revealing that

$$f_j = F_j, \quad j = 5, 6, 7, \tag{3-4}$$

$$\mathcal{K}_j = \widetilde{H}_j, \quad j = 3, 4, \tag{3-5}$$

and

$$f_4 = F_4 - \frac{30}{11}\widetilde{H}_4, \tag{3-6}$$

$$f_3 = F_3 - \frac{8}{3}\widetilde{H}_3, \tag{3-7}$$

$$f_2 = F_2 - \frac{5}{7}\nu'' H_3 - \frac{18}{7}\widetilde{H}_2 - \frac{5}{33}(7\nu''^2 + 17)\widetilde{H}_4, \tag{3-8}$$

$$f_1 = F_1 - \frac{3}{5}\nu'' H_2 - \frac{12}{5}\widetilde{H}_1 - \frac{1}{7}(5\nu''^2 + 13)\widetilde{H}_3; \tag{3-9}$$

$$h_3 = H_3 + \frac{42}{11}\nu''\widetilde{H}_4, \tag{3-10}$$

$$h_2 = H_2 + \frac{10}{3}\nu''\widetilde{H}_3, \tag{3-11}$$

$$h_1 = H_1 + \frac{3}{7}H_3 + \frac{18}{7}\nu''\widetilde{H}_2 + \frac{28}{11}\nu''\widetilde{H}_4, \tag{3-12}$$

$$h_0 = H_0 + \frac{1}{5}H_2 + \frac{6}{5}\nu''\widetilde{H}_1 + \frac{20}{21}\nu''\widetilde{H}_3; \tag{3-13}$$

$$\mathcal{K}_2 = \widetilde{H}_2 + \frac{10}{11}\widetilde{H}_4, \tag{3-14}$$

$$\mathcal{K}_1 = \widetilde{H}_1 + \frac{2}{3}\widetilde{H}_3, \tag{3-15}$$

$$\mathcal{K}_0 = \widetilde{H}_0 + \frac{2}{7}\widetilde{H}_2 + \frac{7}{33}\widetilde{H}_4; \tag{3-16}$$

equations (3-3) can be solved for $\mathcal{K}_j(a_1)$ to yield

$$\mathcal{K}_4(a_1) = \gamma_4 b_6^{(2,4)} f_4 g_2 \ , \tag{3-17}$$

$$\mathcal{K}_3(a_1) = \gamma_3 b_5^{(2,3)} f_3 g_2 \ , \tag{3-18}$$

$$\mathcal{K}_2(a_1) = \gamma_2 \left\{ b_4^{(2,2)} f_2 g_2 + \frac{20}{11} C^{(2,4)} \right\} , \tag{3-19}$$

$$\mathcal{K}_1(a_1) = \frac{4}{3} \gamma_1 C^{(2,3)} \ , \tag{3-20}$$

$$\mathcal{K}_0(a_1) = \frac{4}{7} \gamma_0 \left\{ C^{(2,3)} + \frac{19}{33} C^{(2,4)} \right\} , \tag{3-21}$$

where $b_j^{(i,k)}$ continues to denote the surface values of the function defined by equation (2-16) of Chapter III , $C^{(i,k)}$ denotes the surface values of the function

$$C^{i,k}(a) = (\eta_2 + \eta_j) f_j g_2 - \mathcal{K}_j \ , \tag{3-22}$$

and γ_j , the surface values of

$$\gamma_j(a) = \frac{1}{j + 2 + \dfrac{a}{\mathcal{K}_j}\left(\dfrac{\partial \mathcal{K}_j}{\partial a}\right)} \ . \tag{3-23}$$

Similarly, a solution of equation (3-2) yields, at the surface,

$$h_3(a_1) = 42 \delta_3 \nu'' C^{(2,4)} \tag{3-24}$$

$$h_2(a_1) = 30 \delta_2 \nu'' C^{(2,3)} \ , \tag{3-25}$$

$$h_1(a_1) = \delta_1 \{ [9 C^{(2,2)} + \frac{86}{11} C^{(2,4)}] \nu'' - 3 h_3 \} \ , \tag{3-26}$$

$$h_0(a_1) = \delta_0 \{ 2 [\frac{23}{21} C^{(2,3)} - 3 h_1] \nu'' - h_2 \} \ , \tag{3-27}$$

where the δ_j's stand for the surface values of the function

$$\delta_j(a) = \frac{2}{2j + 5} \left\{ \frac{1}{j + 1 + \dfrac{a}{h_j}\left(\dfrac{dh_j}{da}\right)} \right\} ; \tag{3-28}$$

and, lastly, a solution of (2-1) yields

$$f_4(a_1) = -\frac{20}{33} \Delta_4 C^{(2,4)} \ , \tag{3-29}$$

$$f_3(a_1) = -\frac{16}{21}\Delta_3 C^{(2,3)} , \tag{3-30}$$

$$f_2(a_1) = -\frac{2}{7}\Delta_2\left\{\frac{18}{5}C^{(2,2)} - \frac{2}{33}(14\nu''^2-65)C^{(2,4)} - h_3\nu''\right\}, \tag{3-31}$$

$$f_1(a_1) = \frac{2}{5}\Delta_1\left\{4h_1 + \frac{2}{21}(10\nu''^2 - 37)C^{(2,3)} + h_4\nu''\right\}, \tag{3-32}$$

where, as in our previous work,

$$\Delta_j = \frac{2j+1}{j + \frac{a}{f_j}\left(\frac{df_j}{da}\right)} . \tag{3-33}$$

Needless to stress, the foregoing values of $f_j(a_1)$ arise solely from the interaction between rotation and tides and are, therefore, additive to the purely tidal terms as represented by equations (2-17)-(2-23) of Chapter III; and our present value of $\mathcal{K}_0(a_1)$ is likewise to be added to the purely rotational value of $f_2(a_1)$ as given by equation (5-18) of Chapter III. Moreover (as there are no non-vanishing $\mathcal{F}_j$'s for $j > 4$ within the scheme of our approximation), interaction between rotation and tides is limited to spherical harmonic distortion of orders up to the fourth; the fifth, sixth and seventh harmonic is controlled by tides alone.

Ultimately, the value of f_0 follows again from the requirement that the mass of the distorted configuration should continue to be constant also for any interaction between rotation and tides. When the generalized radius-vector r' is inserted in equation (1-25) of Chapter III for the mass, it follows at once that

$$f_0 = -\frac{1}{5}f_2^2 - \frac{1}{7}f_3^2 - \frac{1}{3}\nu'' h_1 + \frac{3}{5}(\nu''^2 - 1)h_2 , \tag{3-34}$$

where f_2, f_3 are now purely tidal, and h_1, h_2 the interaction terms. The second-order rotational term denoted by $\mathcal{K}_0$ in (1-37) remains, moreover, unaffected by tides and continues to be identical with that given by equation (1-40).

Such being the case, our solution for the surface values of amplitudes of all spherical harmonics on the right-hand side of equation (1-37) for the radius-vector is then complete, and the external form a fluid configuration distorted by axial rotation and tidal pull from any direction is known in full generality as far as quantities of the order of squares of the superficial distortion are concerned. When terms of purely rotational or tidal origin (investigated already in Chapters II and III) are added to the interaction terms investigated in the present chapter, this form will be the resultant of a superposition of fourteen partial tides of known amplitude and period.

In certain special cases the total number of partial tides can be somewhat reduced. Thus if the axis of rotation of our fluid configuration becomes perpendicular to the orbital plane of the tide-generating body, the direction cosine $\nu'' = 0$. If so, however, all the h_j's become identically zero, and the radius-vector ceases to contain any terms varying as $P_1(\nu)\,P_j(\cos\Theta)$; the number of partial tides being thus reduced from 14 to 11.

Another far-reaching simplification obtains if the internal structure of our configuration is such that the density-gradient remains negligible throughout the interior—i.e., if the configuration is homogeneous (ρ = constant), or again infinitely condensed ($\rho = 0$ everywhere except at the center). In such a case it follows at once from the respective Clairaut equation that

$$\mathscr{h}_j = (\eta_2 + \eta_j) f_j g_2 \tag{3-35}$$

for $j = 2, 3, 4,$ and, in consequence,

$$\mathscr{h}_1 = \mathscr{h}_0 = 0 \tag{3-36}$$

throughout the interior. If so, however, all the constants $C^{(i,j)}$ as defined by equation (2-22) then vanish identically, and so do all h_j's as well as f_j's as represented by equations (3-24)-(3-27) and (3-29)-(3-32). The total effect of interaction between rotation and tides reduces then to three distinct terms, varying as $P_2^2(\nu)\,P_j(\cos\Theta)$ for $j = 2, 3, 4,$ whose amplitudes are given by the foregoing equation (3-35). The total number of partial tides has thus been reduced to 10—irrespective of whether the axis of rotation is perpendicular or inclined to the orbital plane.

IV-4: EXTERIOR POTENTIAL: INTERACTION TERMS

Having expressed the external form of a fluid configuration distorted by rotation and tides correctly to quantities of second order in the most general form, it remains now to do the same for the potential V exerted by this configuration on an arbitrary external point. In order to do so, let us return to equation (2-2) and evaluate the contributions $V_n(a_1)$ arising from interaction between rotation and tides with the aid of the appropriate Clairaut's equations (2-31)-(2-33).

It is evident from the structure of these equations that, for $a = a_1$,

$$\int_0^{a_1} \rho \frac{\partial}{\partial a}(a^{j+3} F_j)\,da = (2j+1) a_1^{\,j} \left\{ a \frac{\partial}{\partial a}(\mathscr{F}_j) - F_j \right\}_{a_1} , \tag{4-1}$$

$$\int_0^{a_1} \rho \frac{\partial}{\partial a}(a^{j+4} H_j)\,da = (2j+3) a_1^{\,j+1} \left\{ a \frac{\partial}{\partial a}(\mathscr{G}_j) - H_j \right\}_{a_1} , \tag{4-2}$$

and

$$\int_0^{a_1} \rho \frac{\partial}{\partial a}(a^{j+5}\widetilde{H}_j)da = (2j+5)a_1^{j+2}\left\{a\frac{\partial}{\partial a}(\mathscr{H}_j) - \widetilde{H}_j\right\}_{a_1} , \tag{4-3}$$

respectively. The values of $F_j(a_1)$, $H_j(a_1)$ or $\widetilde{H}_j(a_1)$ are now obtainable from equations (2-14)-(2-30) in which we have inserted for $f_j(a_1)$ from (3-29)-(3-32), for $h_j(a_1)$ from (3-24)-(3-27), and for $h_j(a_1)$ from (3-17)-(3-21) as established in the preceding section. Moreover, a determination of surface values of the functions $\mathscr{F}_j$, $\mathscr{G}_j$ and $\mathscr{H}_j$ as defined by equations (2-34)-(2-46) should likewise create no difficulty.

Therefore, the general expression for the contributions, to the exterior potential $V(a_1)$, of interaction between rotation and tides should be expressible as

$$V = G\frac{m_1}{r}\left\{1 + \ldots + \sum_{n=1}^{7}\left(\frac{a_1}{r}\right)^n \ell_{j,k}^{(i)n} P_j^i(\nu) P_k(\cos\Theta)\right\} , \tag{4-4}$$

where the constants $\ell_{j,k}^{(i)n}$ are defined by the equation

$$\int_0^{a_1} \rho \frac{\partial}{\partial a}\left\{a^{n+3}\Phi_{j,k}^{(i)n}\right\}da = (2n+1)a_1^n \ell_{j,k}^{(i)n}\int_0^a \rho a^2 da , \tag{4-5}$$

and the Φ-functions are as given by equations (2-5)-(2-13). Evaluating them we find (after some algebra) the coefficients $\ell_{j,k}^{(i)n}$ in the foregoing expansion (4-4) to assume the forms

$$\ell_{0,1}^{(0)1} = \frac{3}{5}h_2\nu'' + \frac{12}{5}\kappa_1 + \frac{9}{35}(5\nu''^2 - 1)C^{(2,3)} , \tag{4-6}$$

$$\ell_{0,2}^{(0)2} = \frac{5}{7}h_3\nu'' - \frac{18}{7}C^{(2,3)} + \frac{5}{21}(7\nu''^2 - 1)C^{(2,4)} , \tag{4-7}$$

$$\ell_{0,3}^{(0)3} = -\frac{8}{3}C^{(2,3)} , \tag{4-8}$$

$$\ell_{0,4}^{(0)4} = -\frac{30}{11}C^{(2,4)} ; \tag{4-9}$$

$$\ell_{0,0}^{(0)2} = -\frac{1}{3}\nu''h_1 + \frac{1}{7}\nu''h_3 - \frac{2}{7}(3\nu''^2 + 2)C^{(2,2)} + \frac{2}{21}(5\nu''^2 + 1)C^{(2,4)} \tag{4-10}$$

$$\ell_{0,1}^{(0)3} = -\frac{3}{5}\nu''h_2 - \frac{12}{5}\kappa_1 - \frac{2}{5}(5\nu''^2 + 4)C^{(2,3)} , \tag{4-11}$$

$$\ell_{0,2}^{(0)4} = -\frac{5}{7}\nu''h_3 + \frac{18}{7}C^{(2,2)} - \frac{30}{77}(7\nu''^2 + 6)C^{(2,4)} , \tag{4-12}$$

$$\ell^{(0)5}_{0,3} = + \frac{8}{3} C^{(2,3)} , \tag{4-13}$$

$$\ell^{(0)6}_{0,4} = + \frac{30}{11} C^{(2,4)} , \tag{4-14}$$

$$\ell^{(0)4}_{0,0} = -\frac{1}{7}\nu'' h_3 + \frac{9}{35}(\nu''^2 + 3) C^{(2,2)} - \frac{6}{77}(10\nu''^2 + 9) C^{(2,4)} , \tag{4-15}$$

$$\ell^{(0)5}_{0,1} = + \frac{1}{7}(5\nu''^2 + 13) C^{(2,3)} \tag{4-16}$$

$$\ell^{(0)6}_{0,2} = + \frac{5}{33}(7\nu''^2 + 17) C^{(2,4)} ; \tag{4-17}$$

$$\ell^{(0)6}_{0,0} = + \frac{10}{33}(\nu''^2 + 2) C^{(2,4)} ; \tag{4-18}$$

$$\ell^{(0)1}_{1,0} = h_0 - \frac{1}{5} h_2 - \frac{6}{5} h_1 \nu'' - \frac{18}{35}\nu'' C^{(2,3)} , \tag{4-19}$$

$$\ell^{(0)2}_{1,1} = h_1 - \frac{3}{7} h_3 + \frac{18}{7}\nu'' C^{(2,2)} - \frac{10}{7}\nu'' C^{(2,4)} , \tag{4-20}$$

$$\ell^{(0)3}_{1,2} = h_2 + \frac{10}{3}\nu'' C^{(2,3)} , \tag{4-21}$$

$$\ell^{(0)4}_{1,3} = h_3 + \frac{42}{11}\nu'' C^{(2,4)} ; \tag{4-22}$$

$$\ell^{(0)3}_{1,0} = \frac{1}{5} h_2 + \frac{6}{5} h_1 \nu'' + \frac{22}{15}\nu'' C^{(2,3)} , \tag{4-23}$$

$$\ell^{(0)4}_{1,1} = \frac{3}{7} h_3 - \frac{18}{7}\nu'' C^{(2,2)} + \frac{306}{77}\nu'' C^{(2,4)} , \tag{4-24}$$

$$\ell^{(0)5}_{1,2} = -\frac{10}{3}\nu'' C^{(2,3)} , \tag{4-25}$$

$$\ell^{(0)6}_{1,3} = -\frac{42}{11}\nu'' C^{(2,4)} ; \tag{4-26}$$

$$\ell^{(0)5}_{1,0} = -\frac{20}{21}\nu'' C^{(2,3)} , \tag{4-27}$$

$$\ell^{(0)6}_{1,1} = -\frac{28}{11}\nu'' C^{(2,4)} ; \tag{4-28}$$

$$\ell_{2,0}^{(2)2} = \frac{2}{7}C^{(2,2)} - \frac{1}{21}C^{(2,4)} , \qquad (4\text{-}29)$$

$$\ell_{2,1}^{(2)3} = \kappa_1 + \frac{2}{3}C^{(2,3)} , \qquad (4\text{-}30)$$

$$\ell_{2,2}^{(2)4} = -C^{(2,2)} + \frac{10}{11}C^{(2,4)} , \qquad (4\text{-}31)$$

$$\ell_{2,3}^{(2)5} = -C^{(2,3)} , \qquad (4\text{-}32)$$

$$\ell_{2,4}^{(2)6} = -C^{(2,4)} ; \qquad (4\text{-}33)$$

$$\ell_{2,0}^{(2)4} = -\frac{2}{7}C^{(2,2)} + \frac{20}{77}C^{(2,4)} , \qquad (4\text{-}34)$$

$$\ell_{2,1}^{(2)5} = -\frac{2}{3}C^{(2,3)} , \qquad (4\text{-}35)$$

$$\ell_{2,2}^{(2)6} = -\frac{10}{11}C^{(2,4)} ; \qquad (4\text{-}36)$$

$$\ell_{2,0}^{(2)6} = -\frac{7}{33}C^{(2,4)} . \qquad (4\text{-}37)$$

It should again be pointed out that the coefficients $\ell_{0,j}^{(0)j}$ given above superpose upon the coefficients k_j of the expansion on the right-hand side of equation (2-39) of Chapter III, as given by equations (2-42)-(2-48) of that chapter, in the case of purely tidal origin, and should be added to them; likewise, the coefficient $\ell_{2,0}^{(2)2}$ should be added to the purely rotational k_2, as given by equation (5-27) of Chapter III, in order to obtain the complete expression for the desired expansion of the exterior potential.

IV-5: CLAIRAUT EQUATIONS FOR INTERACTION TERMS

The expressions for the external form and potential of a configuration distorted simultaneously by the rotation and tides, as obtained in the preceding sections IV-3 and 4, do not represent yet the explicit solution of our problem; for the desired amplitudes of the requisite partial tides (as well as the potential terms arising therefrom) are factored by the constants δ_j, $\mathcal{S}_j$ or Δ_j as defined by equations (3-23), (3-28), (3-33); and these cannot be evaluated until the surface values of the logarithmic derivatives of the functions $f_j(a)$, $h_j(a)$ and $\mathcal{K}_j(a)$ have been established for configurations of given structure. The aim of this concluding section of the present report will be to outline a process by which this can be accomplished.

In order to specify, not only the surface values of the amplitudes f_j, h_j, h_j as we have already done in section IV-3, but the whole march of their variation throughout the interior, let us return to equations (3-1)-(3-3) at the outset of the preceding section. If we divide them, respectively, by a^{j+1}, a^{j+2}, a^{j+3}, differentiate with respect to a, and multiply by a^{j+2}, a^{j+3} and a^{j+4}, we readily find that the functions F_j, H_j and $\widetilde{H}_j$ should satisfy the following non-homogeneous linear differential equations

$$a^2F''_j + 6\frac{\rho}{\bar{\rho}}(aF'_j + F_j) - j(j+1)F_j$$

$$= a\frac{\partial}{\partial a}\{a^2\mathscr{F}''_j - j(j+1)\mathscr{F}_j\} + 6\frac{\rho}{\bar{\rho}}\frac{\partial}{\partial a}(a^2\mathscr{F}'_j) \qquad (5\text{-}1)$$

$$+ 3\frac{a\rho'}{\bar{\rho}}a\mathscr{F}'_j \,,$$

$$a^2H''_{j-1} + 6\frac{\rho}{\bar{\rho}}(aH'_{j-1} + H_{j-1}) - j(j+1)H_{j-1}$$

$$= \nu''a\frac{\partial}{\partial a}\{a^2\mathscr{G}''_{j-1} - j(j+1)\mathscr{G}_{j-1}\} + 6\nu''\frac{\rho}{\bar{\rho}}\frac{\partial}{\partial a}(a^2\mathscr{G}'_{j-1})$$

$$+ 3\nu''\frac{a\rho'}{\bar{\rho}}a\mathscr{G}'_{j-1}, \qquad (5\text{-}2)$$

and

$$a^2\widetilde{H}''_{j-2} + 6\frac{\rho}{\bar{\rho}}(a\widetilde{H}_{j-2} + \widetilde{H}_{j-2}) - j(j+1)\widetilde{H}_{j-2}$$

$$= a\frac{\partial}{\partial a}\{a^2\mathscr{H}''_{j-2} - j(j+1)\mathscr{H}_{j-2}\} + 6\frac{\rho}{\bar{\rho}}\frac{\partial}{\partial a}(a^2\mathscr{H}'_{j-2}) \qquad (5\text{-}3)$$

$$+ 3\frac{a\rho'}{\bar{\rho}}a\mathscr{H}'_{j-2} \,,$$

of second order, where the functions $\mathscr{F}_j$, $\mathscr{G}_j$, and $\mathscr{H}_j$ continue to be given by equations (2-34)-(2-46), and accents denote differentiation with respect to a. Moreover, if—as before

$$\frac{\rho}{\bar{\rho}} = D \,, \qquad (5\text{-}4)$$

its differentiation reveals that

$$\frac{a\rho'}{\bar{\rho}} = a\,D' + 3D(D-1) \; . \qquad (5\text{-}5)$$

In order to reduce the right-hand sides of equations (5-1)-(5-3) to more explicit forms, let us recall that all functions $\mathscr{F}_j$, $\mathscr{G}_j$, $\mathscr{H}_j$ as defined by equations (2-34)-(2-46) constitute linear combinations of the products $f_j g_2$ $(j = 2, 3, 4)$. Now

$$\left\{ a\frac{\partial}{\partial a}\left(a^2\frac{\partial^2}{\partial a^2}\right) + 6\frac{\rho}{\bar{\rho}}\frac{\partial}{\partial a}\left(a^2\frac{\partial}{\partial a}\right) + \left[3\frac{a\rho'}{\bar{\rho}} - j(j+1)\right] a\frac{\partial}{\partial a} \right\} f_j g_2$$

$$\begin{aligned} = \; & \{2[2\eta_2\eta_j + j(j-1)\eta_2 - 2(j-3)\eta_j] \\ & - 3D[8\eta_2\eta_j + 9(\eta_2 + \eta_j)] \\ & + 9D^2[\eta_2 + \eta_j] - 3aD'[\eta_2 + \eta_j + 4]\} f_j g_2 \end{aligned} \qquad (5\text{-}6)$$

and, on the other hand, the F_j's , H_j's and $\widetilde{H}_j$'s constitute linear combinations of the desired amplitudes f_j , h_j and $\hbar_j$ as given by equations (2-14)-(2-30). If we introduce their inverted forms (3-4)-(3-16) in equations (5-1)-(5-3), the latter can eventually be reduced to the forms

$$a^2 f''_j + 6D(a f'_j + f_j) - j(j+1)f_j = X_j^{(0)} \; , \qquad (5\text{-}7)$$

$$a^2 h''_j + 6D(a h'_j + h_j) - (j+1)(j+2)h_j = \nu'' Y_j^{(0)} \; , \qquad (5\text{-}8)$$

and

$$\begin{aligned} & a^2\hbar''_j + 6D(a\hbar'_j + \hbar_j) - (j+2)(j+3)\hbar_j \\ & \quad = Z_j^{(0)} - 3DZ_j^{(1)} + (3D)^2 Z_j^{(2)} - (3aD')Z_j^{(3)} \; , \end{aligned} \qquad (5\text{-}9)$$

where the coefficients X_j , Y_j and Z_j are given by

$$\begin{aligned} X_1^{(0)} = \; & 90(\eta_2+\eta_3)f_3 g_2 \\ & - 4(13 + 5\nu''^2)\widetilde{H} - 24\widetilde{H}_1 - 6\nu'' H_2 \; , \end{aligned} \qquad (5\text{-}10)$$

$$\begin{aligned} X_2^{(0)} = \; & 36(\eta_2+\eta_2)f_2 g_2 + 60(\eta_2+\eta_4)f_4 g_2 \\ & - \frac{60}{11}(17 + 7\nu''^2)\widetilde{H}_4 - 36\widetilde{H}_2 - 10\nu'' H_3 \; , \end{aligned} \qquad (5\text{-}11)$$

$$X_3^{(0)} = 48(\eta_2+\eta_3)f_3g_2 \qquad - 48\widetilde{H}_3 , \tag{5-12}$$

$$X_4^{(0)} = 60(\eta_2+\eta_4)f_4g_2 \qquad - 60\widetilde{H}_4 ; \tag{5-13}$$

$$Y_0^{(0)} = \qquad - 12(\eta_2+\eta_3)f_3g_2 + 12\widetilde{H}_1 + \frac{80}{3}\widetilde{H}_3 + 2H_2, \tag{5-14}$$

$$Y_1^{(0)} = -36(\eta_2+\eta_2)f_2g_2 + 36(\eta_2+\eta_4)f_4g_2 + 36\widetilde{H}_2 + 56\widetilde{H}_4 , \tag{5-15}$$

$$Y_2^{(0)} = -60(\eta_2+\eta_3)f_3g_2 \qquad + 60\widetilde{H}_3 , \tag{5-16}$$

$$Y_3^{(0)} = -84(\eta_2+\eta_4)f_4g_2 \qquad + 80\widetilde{H}_4 ; \tag{5-17}$$

and

$$Z_4^{(0)} = 4(\eta_2\eta_4 + 6\eta_2 - \eta_4)f_4g_2 , \tag{5-18}$$

$$Z_3^{(0)} = 4(\eta_2\eta_3 + 3\eta_2)f_3g_2 , \tag{5-19}$$

$$Z_2^{(0)} = 4(\eta_2^2 + 2\eta_2)f_2g_2 - 20(\eta_2+\eta_4)f_4g_2 + 20\widetilde{H}_4 , \tag{5-20}$$

$$Z_1^{(0)} = \qquad - 12(\eta_2+\eta_3)f_3g_2 + 12\widetilde{H}_3 , \tag{5-21}$$

$$Z_0^{(0)} = -4(\eta_2+\eta_4)f_4g_2 - 4(\eta_2+\eta_2)f_2g_2 + 4\widetilde{H}_2 + \frac{84}{11}\widetilde{H}_4 ; \tag{5-22}$$

while

$$Z_j^{(1)} = \begin{cases} 8\eta_2\eta_j + 9(\eta_2+\eta_j) , & j = 2, 3, 4 , \\ 0 , & j = 0, 1 ; \end{cases} \tag{5-23}$$

$$Z_j^{(2)} = \begin{cases} \eta_2 + \eta_j , & j = 2, 3, 4 , \\ 0 , & j = 0, 1 ; \end{cases} \tag{5-24}$$

$$Z_j^{(3)} = \begin{cases} \eta_2 + \eta_j + 4 , & j = 2, 3, 4 , \\ 0 , & j = 0, 1 ; \end{cases} \tag{5-25}$$

respectively.

The remaining problem for computation is now simple. With the functions $\eta_j(a)$, $f_j(a)$ and $g_2(a)$ known from the "first approximation", equations (5-7)-(5-9) can be solved (numerically or otherwise) for

h_j , $\hbar_j$ and f_j in that order, and in order of diminishing j (i.e., 4, 3, 2, 1, 0), and their logarithmic derivatives puts us at least in a position to ascertain the appropriate values of the constants δ_j , δ_j and Δ_j as defined by equations (3-23)-(3-28) and (3-33), and thus to render our whole solution completely explicit.

This concludes, therefore, the specification of the external potential as well as the form (or surface gravity) of a fluid configuration of arbitrary internal structure, distorted simultaneously by rotation and tides to the second order in terms of the superficial distortion. An application of this knowledge for the interpretation of light changes or dynamics of the components in close binary systems, or of the orbital perturbations of artificial satellites revolving in the proximity of the terrestrial globe is now ready to proceed. Its details are, however, outside the scope of this monograph, and must be postponed for subsequent investigation.

IV-6: MOMENTS OF INERTIA

In conclusion of our present discussion of the interaction effects between rotation and tides, the last task outstanding should again be to formulate explicitly the contributions to the principal moments of inertia arising from such an interaction. In order to fix our ideas, suppose that we set out to do so for the moments taken with respect to the axes of symmetry of the tidal distortion (i.e., obtaining if we identify the x-axis of our rectangular system with the line joining the centers of the distorted and disturbing configuration).

If so, the equations (8-2)-(9-9) of Chapter III continue to hold good, of course, and so do the results represented by equations (8-16)-(8-19) of the same chapter, if the f_j's occurring in them are identified with the"interaction" f's similarly denoted on the right-hand side of equation (1-37). The expressions for A" , B" , and C" as given by equation (8-16)-(8-17) of Chapter III are, however, complete only in the case of purely tidal distortion, and remain to be augmented by additional terms arising not only from the "interaction" f's , but also from the h_j's , $\hbar_j$'s and $\hbar_0$ on the right-hand side of (1-37) if our configuration is distorted simultaneously by rotation and tides; and these remain yet to be evaluated.

In order to do so, let us fall back on the general equations (8-2) to (8-9) of Chapter III and insert merely for r' from (1-37) of this chapter, in place of the equations (1-1) or (5-1) of Chapter III relevant to a purely rotational or tidal distortion. In order to facilitate their evaluation, suppose that we change over from the angular coordinates θ, ϕ to the direction cosines λ, μ, ν (as defined by equations 1-1) to serve as our new variables of integration. After some elementary transformations incident to this task we find that the contributions A''_+ , B''_+ , C''_+ arising from the h-terms on the right-hand side of equation (1-37), and additive to those due to the f-terms (as represented by the expressions for A" , B" , C" , given already by the equations 8-16 and 8-17 of the preceding chapter), assume the more explicit forms

$$A''_{+} = 2\pi\int_0^{a_1} \rho\frac{\partial}{\partial a}\left\{a^5\int_{-1}^{1}\int_{-\sqrt{1-\mu^2}}^{\sqrt{1-\mu^2}} \frac{1-\lambda^2}{\lambda}\left[\sum_j P_j(\lambda)\ h_j P_1(\cos\Theta) + \right.\right. \tag{6-1}$$

$$\left.\left. + \hbar_j P_2^2(\cos\Theta) + \hbar_0 P_4^4(\cos\Theta)\right]d\mu d\nu\right\}da ,$$

$$B''_{+} = 2\pi\int_0^{a_1} \rho\frac{\partial}{\partial a}\left\{a^5\int_{-1}^{1}\int_{-\sqrt{1-\mu^2}}^{\sqrt{1-\mu^2}} \frac{1-\mu^2}{\lambda}\left[\sum_j P_j(\lambda)\ h_j P_1(\cos\Theta)\right.\right. \tag{6-2}$$

$$\left.\left. + \hbar_j P_2^2(\cos\Theta) + \hbar_0 P_4^4(\cos\Theta)\right]d\mu d\nu\right\}da ,$$

$$C''_{+} = 2\pi\int_0^{a_1} \rho\frac{\partial}{\partial a}\left\{a^5\int_{-1}^{1}\int_{-\sqrt{1-\mu^2}}^{\sqrt{1-\mu^2}} \frac{1-\nu^2}{\lambda}\left[\sum_j P_j(\lambda)\ h_j P_1(\cos\Theta)\right.\right. \tag{6-3}$$

$$\left.\left. + \hbar_j P_2^2(\cos\Theta) + \hbar_0 P_4^4(\cos\Theta)\right]d\mu d\nu\right\}da ,$$

where, in accordance with equation (5-8) of Chapter II,

$$\cos\Theta = \lambda\lambda' + \mu\mu' + \nu\nu , \tag{6-4}$$

the direction cosines λ', μ', ν' of the axis of rotation (i.e., the Z'-axis) in the doubly-primed equation of coordinates X" Y" Z" introduced in section IV-1 being given by

$$\left.\begin{aligned} \lambda' &= \cos u \sin i , \\ \mu' &= \sin u \sin i , \\ \nu' &= \cos i ; \end{aligned}\right\} \tag{6-5}$$

in which the angles u and i have the same meaning as in equation (1-4). *

The evaluation of the foregoing expressions for A''_+, B''_+, and C''_+ offers again no difficulty; a term-by-term integration reveals that

---

* Equations (6-5) are, therefore, identical with (5-7) of Chapter II if we set $\alpha = u$ and $\beta = i$.

$$A''_+ = 2\pi\int_0^{a_1} \rho \frac{\partial}{\partial a}\left\{ a^5 \left[\frac{5}{2}h_0 + \frac{4}{3}h_1 - \frac{5}{2}h_2 + \frac{4}{7}h_3 \;\lambda' + 4(3+\lambda'^2)\hbar_0 \right.\right.$$

$$+ 5\hbar_1 - \frac{4}{7}(3+5\lambda'^2)\not\hbar_2 - \frac{5}{16}(9+5\lambda'^2)\hbar_3 \qquad (6-6)$$

$$\left.\left. - \frac{8}{21}(1-3\lambda'^2)\hbar_4 + 160(2+\lambda'^2)\not\hbar_0 + \ldots \right]\right\} da ,$$

$$B''_+ = 2\pi\int_0^{a_1} \rho \frac{\partial}{\partial a}\left\{ a^5 \left[\frac{15}{4}h_0 + \frac{8}{3}h_1 + \frac{5}{4}h_2 + \frac{2}{7}h_3 \;\lambda' + 4(3+\mu'^2)\not\hbar_0 \right.\right.$$

$$+ \frac{5}{8}(15 - 7\lambda'^2 - 2\nu'^2)\hbar_1 + \frac{4}{7}(4 - 7\lambda'^2 + 2\nu'^2)\not\hbar_2$$

$$- \frac{5}{64}(5 + 31\lambda'^2 - 14\nu'^2)\not\hbar_3 + \frac{2}{21}(3 - 7\lambda'^2 - 2\nu'^2)\hbar_4 \qquad (6-7)$$

$$\left.\left. + 160(2+\mu'^2)\not\hbar_0 + \ldots \right]\right\} da ,$$

$$C''_+ = 2\pi\int_0^{a_1} \rho \frac{\partial}{\partial a}\left\{ a^5 \left[\frac{15}{4}h_0 + \frac{8}{3}h_1 + \frac{5}{4}h_2 + \frac{2}{7}h_3 \;\lambda' + 4(3+\nu'^2)\not\hbar_0 \right.\right.$$

$$+ \frac{5}{8}(13-5\lambda'^2+2\nu'^2)\hbar_1 + \frac{4}{7}(6-9\lambda'^2-2\nu'^2)\hbar_2$$

$$+ \frac{5}{64}(9-45\lambda'^2-14\nu'^2)\not\hbar_3 + \frac{2}{21}(1-5\lambda'^2+2\nu'^2)\hbar_4 \qquad (6-8)$$

$$\left.\left. + 160(2+\nu'^2)\not\hbar_0 + \ldots \right]\right\} da ,$$

respectively.

The moments of inertia $A'' + A''_+$, $B'' + B''_+$, $C'' + C''_+$, as given now by equations (8-16)-(8-17) of Chapter III augmented by (6-6)-(6-8) of this chapter, are not yet sufficient to specify the total kinetic energy of a configuration distorted by rotation and tides in the doubly-primed system of coordinates. In order to make this possible, it remains for us still to evaluate the products of inertia

$$D = \int yz \, dm' , \qquad (6-9)$$

$$E = \int xz \, dm' , \qquad (6-10)$$

$$F = \int xy \, dm' , \qquad (6-11)$$

in which the mass element dm' as well as the limits of integration continue to be given by equations (8-5)-(8-6) of the preceding chapter.

If we rewrite them now again in terms of the direction cosines λ, μ, ν, as the new variables of integration, the resulting expressions for D'', E'', and F'' will be exactly of the same form as those for A''_+, B''_+, and C''_+ as given by equations (6-1)-(6-3), provided only that the quadratic binomials

$$1-\lambda^2 , \qquad 1-\mu^2 , \qquad 1-\nu^2$$

immediately behind the last integral sign on the right-hand side of those equations are replaced by the products

$$\mu\nu , \qquad \lambda\nu , \qquad \lambda\mu ,$$

respectively.

Performing the actual integration we thus find that

$$D'' = 2\pi \int_0^{a_1} \rho \frac{\partial}{\partial a} \left\{ a^5 \left[4\hbar_0 + \frac{5}{4}\hbar_1 + \frac{8}{7}\hbar_2 - \frac{35}{32}\hbar_3 + \frac{4}{21}\hbar_4 \; \mu'\nu' \right.\right. \qquad (6-12)$$
$$\left.\left. + \, 40\mu'\nu'(3-2\lambda'^2)\hbar_0 + \ldots \right] \right\} da ,$$

$$E'' = 2\pi \int_0^{a_1} \rho \frac{\partial}{\partial a} \left\{ a^5 \left[\frac{5}{4}h_0 + \frac{2}{3}h_1 - \frac{2}{7}h_3 \;\; \nu' \right.\right.$$
$$+ \, 4\hbar_0 + \frac{5}{2}\hbar_1 + \frac{4}{7}\hbar_2 - \frac{5}{8}\hbar_3 - \frac{16}{21}\hbar_4 \;\; \lambda'\mu' \qquad (6-13)$$
$$\left.\left. + \, 40\lambda'\mu'(3-2\mu'^2)\hbar_0 + \ldots \right] \right\} da ,$$

and

$$F'' = 2\pi \int_0^{a_1} \rho \frac{\partial}{\partial a} \left\{ a^5 \left[\frac{5}{4}h_0 + \frac{2}{3}h_1 - \frac{2}{7}h \;\; \mu' \right.\right.$$
$$+ \, 4\hbar_0 + \frac{5}{2}\hbar_1 + \frac{4}{7}\hbar_2 - \frac{5}{8}\hbar_3 - \frac{16}{21}\hbar_4 \;\; \lambda'\nu' \qquad (6-14)$$
$$\left.\left. + \, 40\lambda'\nu'(3-2\nu'^2)\hbar_0 + \ldots \right] \right\} da ,$$

respectively. The reader may notice that the coefficients of μ' and ν' on the right-hand sides of equations (6-13) and (6-14) for E'' and F'' are identical; and so are those of $\lambda'\mu'$ and $\lambda'\nu'$. If, moreover, the axis of rotation of our configuration happens to be perpendicular to the orbital plane (i.e., $\lambda' = \mu' = 0$ and $\nu' = 1$), all terms on the right-hand sides of the foregoing equations (6-12)-(6-14) will vanish except for those containing h_j in (6-13). But in section IV-3 we found that, in this case, all h_j's vanish identically; and if so, all three products of inertia become—as they should—equal to zero; the moments of inertia being sufficient to specify the kinetic energy of our configuration to the requisite degree of accuracy.

V

NON-RADIAL OSCILLATIONS

Throughout all preceding chapters of this monograph, a distortion of self-gravitating fluid configurations by rotation or tides has been considered strictly as a hydrostatic problem (and the amount of distortion as constant). This should, in general, be true as long as the coefficients $c_{i,j}$ in the expansion of the disturbing potential $V'(r')$ in the Clairaut's equation are independent of the time. In the sense of a purely rotational distortion this should indeed be true to a very high degree of accuracy; for the velocities of axial rotation of the Earth, other planets, or the stars are known to be virtually uniform and to alter or fluctuate only at an excessively slow rate.

When it comes, however, to the tidal distortion, the same will be true only provided that the relative orbit of the tide-generating body is circular, and its radius-vector R can be regarded as constant. It is, however, well known from the dynamical problem of two bodies (and amply attested by astronomical observations) that the most general form of their orbits is an ellipse, characterized by a radius-vector

$$R = \frac{A(1-e^2)}{1 + e \cos v} = A(1 - e \cos E) , \qquad (0-1)$$

where A denotes the semi-major axis of the relative orbit; e , its eccentricity; and v or E the true or eccentric anomaly of the disturbing body measured from the periastron passage, and related with the time t by Kepler's well-known equation

$$E - e \sin E = (2\pi/P)(t-t_0) = M , \qquad (0-2)$$

where P denotes the period of the orbit; t , the time of the periastron passage; and M , the mean anomaly.

Unless $e = 0$, the radius-vector R in an elliptic orbit becomes a function of the time as defined by the foregoing equations (0-1) and (0-2). In sections II-5 and III-4 we found, however, that the amplitude of the j-th tidal harmonic distortion was inversely proportional to (and varies with the time as) R^{j+1} . Now according to a well-known expansion of the elliptic motion,

$$\frac{A}{R} = 1 + 2\sum_{n=1}^{\infty} J_n(ne)\cos n M \ , \qquad (0\text{-}3)$$

where $J_n(x)$ denotes the Bessel function of the first kind and order n. When we raise this series to the $(j+1)$-st power and insert in equations (5-17) or (4-14) of Chapter II or III, we find that the respective coefficients c_j become periodic functions of the time (with amplitudes depending on the orbital eccentricity), oscillating in the period P and its submultiples.

If this is so, however, to what extent does the purely hydrostatic treatment of our subject so far continue to be applicable? A well-known theorem of dynamics (due originally to Young) asserts that, even if the coefficients c_j of the disturbing potential do depend on the time, our problem can still be treated as hydrostatic provided that the periods of the respective free non-radial oscillations of the distorted configurations are sufficiently short in comparison with the period of the disturbing force (to enable our configuration to adjust its form to the field of force prevailing at any moment). Whenever this is the case, the resultant tidal distortion will continue to be given by the equilibrium theory of tides developed in this volume. In the contrary case, the time-dependence of the c_j's would force us to restore the time-dependent terms also in the equations of motion as well—and their solution would lead to the development of a dynamical theory of tides, which is wholly outside the scope of this monograph.

If, however, we wish to remain within the confines of the equilibrium theory of tides, what assurance do we have that the free periods of such structure as can be encountered among the stars or palets are indeed sufficiently short in comparison with oscillations of the disturbing force? A glance at the expansion on the right-hand side of equation (0-3) makes it evident that the Fourier development of $R^{-(j+1)}$ is bound to contain terms whose periods become arbitrarily small submultiples of that of the orbit, though their amplitudes are again likely to be small. If, however, any one of these submultiples becomes identical with (or very close to) a free period of non-radial oscillation, its amplitude—no matter how small it originally may have been—could be enhanced by resonance (or a close approach to it) to give rise to phenomena departing significantly from the equilibrium theory of tides.

In considering such a possibility, our first task should be to investigate the frequency spectrum of free non-radial oscillations of self-gravitating fluids, and to compare them with the period P of the disturbing tidal force which, according to Kepler's third law, should be given by the equation

$$\frac{4\pi^2}{P^2} = \frac{G(m_1 + m_2)}{A^3} \ . \qquad (0\text{-}4)$$

The conclusion that resonance cannot occur (or be even approached) in bodies of astronomical significance except, possibly, for very high (and highly damped) overtones will enable us to close the present volume with confidence that our hydrostatic approach to the theory of equilibrium of the celestial bodies rests indeed on secure foundations.

V-1. NON-RADIAL OSCILLATIONS OF SELF-GRAVITATING FLUIDS

In order to approach our problem, let us consider the oscillations of a compressible gas sphere, under the influence of its own gravity, which are small enough for the squares and higher powers of the amplitudes of the displacement to be ignorable. In setting up the requisite equations of motion we shall, for simplicity, neglect all effects arising from viscosity, and assume the motion of any individual gas particle to take place adiabatically. Let, furthermore, a (vector) displacement $\delta\vec{r}$ of any particle from its position of equilibrium alter the pressure P, density ρ, and gravitational potential W arising from the mass by the amounts δP, $\delta\rho$, and δW, respectively—all small enough for their squares and higher powers to be negligible. If so, then within the scheme of this approximation the linearized Eulerian equations of motion, safeguarding the conservation of momentum, can be written as

$$\rho\frac{\partial^2\delta\vec{r}}{\partial t^2} + \text{grad}\,\delta P + \delta\rho\,\text{grad}\,W + \rho\,\text{grad}\,\delta W = 0 \;; \tag{1-1}$$

and the equation of continuity, safeguarding the conservation of mass, becomes

$$\delta\bar{\rho} + \text{div}\,(\rho\,\delta\vec{r}) = 0 \,. \tag{1-2}$$

Consistent with our assumption of a simply harmonic motion, we shall seek such solutions of the foregoing equations for which

$$\left\{\frac{\partial^2}{\partial t^2} + \sigma^2\right\}\delta\vec{r} = 0 \,, \tag{1-3}$$

where σ denotes the frequency of the respective oscillation.

In order to solve these equations, let us begin by eliminating the time derivative of $\delta\vec{r}$ between equations (1-1) and (1-3). Inserting (1-3) in (1-1) and taking the divergences of both sides, we find that

$$\sigma^2\,\text{div}\,(\rho\,\delta\vec{r}) = \text{div}\,\{\text{grad}\,\delta P + \delta\rho\,\text{grad}\,W + \rho\,\text{grad}\,\delta W\} \,. \tag{1-4}$$

According to the equation of continuity, $\text{div}\,(\rho\,\delta\vec{r}) = -\delta\rho$; while the equation of hydrostatic equilibrium asserts that

$$\text{grad}\,P = -\,\rho\,\text{grad}\,W \,. \tag{1-5}$$

If, furthermore, use is made of the identity

$$\text{div grad } \delta P = \nabla^2 \delta P \ , \tag{1-6}$$

where ∇^2 denotes Laplacian operator, the equations (1-4) of motion can be reduced to

$$\sigma^2 \delta\rho = \text{div}\,\{(\delta\rho/\rho)\text{grad } P\} - \nabla^2 \delta P - \text{div}(\rho \text{ grad } \delta W) \ . \tag{1-7}$$

We wish now to consider such small oscillations of our compressible fluid globe in which $\vec{\delta r}$, δP, and $\delta\rho$ can be decomposed into products of purely radial functions multiplied by a surface harmonic of order j. If so, it follows at once (from Laplace's equation) that

$$\nabla^2 \delta P = \frac{1}{r^2}\frac{\partial}{\partial r}\left\{r^2 \frac{\partial \delta P}{\partial r}\right\} - \frac{j(j+1)}{r^2}\delta P \ , \tag{1-8}$$

and

$$\text{div}\left\{\frac{\delta\rho}{\rho}\text{grad } P\right\} = \frac{1}{r^2}\frac{\partial}{\partial r}\left\{r^2 \frac{\delta\rho}{\rho}\frac{\partial P}{\partial r}\right\}, \tag{1-9}$$

$$\text{div}\,(\rho \text{ grad } \delta W) = \left\{\frac{1}{r^2}\frac{\partial}{\partial r} \quad r^2 \rho \frac{\partial \delta W}{\partial r}\right\} . \tag{1-10}$$

Moreover, the radial component δr of the vector $\vec{\delta r}$ follows from equations (1-1) and (1-3) as

$$\sigma^2 \rho\, \delta r = \frac{\partial \delta P}{\partial r} - \frac{\delta\rho}{\rho}\frac{\partial P}{\partial r} + \rho \frac{\partial \delta W}{\partial r} \ . \tag{1-11}$$

Inserting equations (1-8) to (1-10) in (1-7), we find that

$$\begin{aligned} \delta\rho &= \frac{j(j+1)}{r^2\sigma^2}\{\delta P + \rho\delta W\} - \frac{1}{r^2\sigma^2}\frac{\partial}{\partial r}\left\{r^2\left[\frac{\partial \delta P}{\partial r} - \frac{\delta\rho}{\rho}\frac{\partial P}{\partial r} + \rho\frac{\partial \delta W}{\partial r}\right]\right\} \\ &= \frac{j(j+1)}{r^2\sigma^2}\{\delta P + \delta W\} - \frac{1}{r^2}\frac{\partial}{\partial r}\{r^2 \rho\, \delta r\} \end{aligned} \tag{1-12}$$

by (1-11).

Lastly, the principle of the conservation of energy reveals that, for an ordinary gas, the relation between the adiabatic changes in pressure and density of any element of the fluid will be given by the equation

$$\delta P + \delta r \frac{\partial P}{\partial r} = c^2\left\{\delta\rho + \delta r \frac{\partial \rho}{\partial r}\right\} \tag{1-13}$$

where

$$c^2 = \gamma \frac{P}{\rho} \tag{1-14}$$

denotes the square of the local velocity of sound; and γ , the ratio of specific heats of the fluid.

Equations (1-11), (1-12), and (1-13) constitute the fundamental set of differential equations relating δr , δP , and $\delta\rho$.

In order to solve them, let us remember that, as the total potential W arising from the mass, its disturbed part δW must also satisfy the Poisson equation

$$\frac{\partial}{\partial r}\left\{r^2 \frac{\partial \delta W}{\partial r}\right\} - j(j+1)\delta W = 4\pi G\,\delta\rho \; . \tag{1-15}$$

Now solving (1-12) for δW we obtain

$$j(j+1)\,\rho\,\delta W = r^2\sigma^2\delta\rho - j(j+1)\,\delta P + \sigma^2\frac{\partial}{\partial r}(r^2\rho\,\delta r) \; ; \tag{1-16}$$

while equation (1-11) reveals that

$$\frac{\partial \delta W}{\partial r} = \sigma^2\delta r - \frac{1}{\rho}\frac{\partial \delta P}{\partial r} - \frac{\delta\rho}{\rho^2}\frac{\partial P}{\partial r} \; . \tag{1-17}$$

As, by differentiation of this latter equation and its combination with (1-16) it follows that

$$\frac{1}{r^2}\frac{\partial}{\partial r}\left\{r^2\frac{\partial \delta W}{\partial r}\right\} = \left\{\frac{\partial}{\partial r} + \frac{2}{r}\right\}\left\{\sigma^2\delta r - \frac{1}{\rho}\frac{\partial \delta P}{\partial r} - \frac{\delta\rho}{\rho^2}\frac{\partial P}{\partial r}\right\} , \tag{1-18}$$

an insertion of (1-16) and (1-18) in (1-15) results in

$$\begin{aligned}&\left\{\frac{\partial}{\partial r} + \frac{2}{r}\right\}\left\{\sigma^2\delta r - \frac{1}{\rho}\frac{\partial \delta P}{\partial r} - \frac{\delta\rho}{\rho^2}\frac{\partial P}{\partial r}\right\}\\ &\quad - \sigma^2\frac{\delta\rho}{\rho} + j(j+1)\frac{\delta P}{\rho r^2} - \frac{\sigma^2}{\rho r^2}\frac{\partial}{\partial r}(r^2\rho\,\delta r) = 4\pi G\,\delta\rho \; .\end{aligned} \tag{1-19}$$

On the other hand, a differentiation of (1-16) and a subsequent elimination of $\partial\delta W/\partial r$ between (1-16) and (1-17) yields another relation

$$\begin{aligned}&\frac{\partial}{\partial r}\left\{r^2\sigma^2\frac{\delta\rho}{\rho} - j(j+1)\frac{\delta P}{\rho} + \frac{\sigma^2}{\rho}\frac{\partial}{\partial r}(r^2\rho\,\delta r)\right\}\\ &\quad = \sigma^2\delta r - \frac{1}{\rho}\frac{\partial \delta P}{\partial r} - \frac{\delta\rho}{\rho^2}\frac{\partial P}{\partial r} \; ,\end{aligned} \tag{1-20}$$

which together with (1-19) and (1-13) constitutes our fundamental set of equations in which δW no longer occurs.

Equations (1-19) and (1-20) represent a pair of second-order differential relations for δr and δP or $\delta\rho$ (as one of the two can always be eliminated in favor of the other by means of the adiabatic equation 1-13); and, therefore, a suitable elimination process would, in general, end with differential equation of fourth order for δr , δP , or $\delta\rho$ as function of the radial distance r . The actual details of such an elimination are rather involved and need not be reproduced in this place.* Suffice it to say that the characteristic frequencies of j-th harmonic non-radial oscillations are determined as such values of σ which render the solution of the equations (1-19)-(1-20) consistent with the boundary conditions requiring that, at the center $(r = 0)$,

$$\delta r = \delta P = 0 \tag{1-21}$$

while, at the surface r_1 (such that $\rho(r_1) = 0$)

$$\delta P = \frac{\partial \delta W}{\partial r} + \frac{j(j+1)}{r} \delta W = 0 . \tag{1-22}$$

The reader may note that (unlike in the case of purely radial oscillations, when $j = 0$), the non-radial oscillations $(j \geq 2)$ produce (to the first order in small quantities) no pressure (or density) variations at the center of our configuration; and their central temperature remains, therefore, unchanged.

Our present knowledge of the characteristic solutions of equations (1-19)-(1-20) satisfying the boundary conditions (1-21)-(1-22) for arbitrary density distribution $\rho(r)$ is as yet extremely meager. If ρ = constant, Pekeris** has been the first to show that equations (1-21)-(1-22) are inconsistent for any real values of σ —which means that homogeneous compressible configurations cannot oscillate non-radially. If, however, the nature of the function $\rho(r)$ is such that most part of the mass of our configuration is confined near its center —as is amply true of the stars—the perturbations δW of the self-gravitating potential may become very small; and their neglect may permit us to formulate so restricted an oscillatory problem in essentially simple terms to be developed in the next section.

V-2: NON-RADIAL OSCILLATIONS: STELLAR CASE

If the density concentration inside our configuration is sufficiently high to enable us to ignore the perturbations δW of the gravitational potential due to non-radial oscillations—as can certainly be done to a high degree of approximation for stellar models of all evolutionary stages—a study of their oscillatory properties becomes much simpler. In order to demonstrate it, let us return to equations (1-11) and (1-12) which reduce now to the statements that

* For fuller details cf., e.g., P. Ledoux, Handb. d. Physik, 51 (Astrophysik II), Berlin 1958, pp. 509-538.

* Cf. Ch. Pekeris, Astrophys. Journ., 88, 189, 1938.

$$\sigma^2 \rho\, \delta r = \frac{\partial \delta P}{\partial r} - \frac{\delta\rho}{\rho}\frac{\partial P}{\partial r} \tag{2-1}$$

and

$$\delta\rho = \frac{j(j+1)}{r^2\sigma^2}\delta P - \frac{1}{r^2}\frac{\partial}{\partial r}\{r^2\rho\delta r\} \;; \tag{2-2}$$

while the adiabatic equation (1-13) continues to provide an additional algebraic relation between δr, δP, and $\delta\rho$.

Eliminating $\delta\rho$ from (2-1) and (2-2) by the use of (1-13) we can reduce the former two equations to the form

$$\frac{\partial}{\partial r}(r^2\delta r) - \frac{g}{c^2}r^2\delta r = \left\{\frac{j(j+1)}{\sigma^2} - \frac{r^2}{c^2}\right\}\frac{\delta P}{\rho} \tag{2-3}$$

and

$$\frac{\partial}{\partial r}(\delta P) + \frac{g}{c^2}\delta P = \left\{\sigma^2 + \frac{g}{\rho}\frac{\partial\rho}{\partial r} + \frac{g^2}{c^2}\right\}\rho\,\delta r \;, \tag{2-4}$$

where the local gravity g is related to the pressure gradient by means of the equation

$$\frac{\partial P}{\partial r} = -g\rho \tag{2-5}$$

of hydrostatic equilibrium. A neglect of δW in (1-11) and (1-12) permitted us to reduce the order of our simultaneous differential system (2-3)-(2-4) to one-half (i.e., from the fourth to the second); and, therefore, only two boundary conditions are required to render the solution determinate. These conditions reduce to

$$\delta r = 0 \quad \text{at} \quad r = 0 \tag{2-6}$$

while

$$\delta P = 0 \quad \text{at} \quad r = r_1 \tag{2-7}$$

i.e., to a requirement that there should be no displacement at the center, and no variation of pressure over free surface. These conditions can, in general, be satisfied only for certain discrete values of σ, and their ensemble represents the frequency spectrum of our oscillating configuration.

In order to deduce from (2-3) and (2-4) the equation governing the amplitude δr of the displacement caused by non-radial oscillations, let us introduce a new dependent variable v, defined by

$$v = r^2(\delta r)P^{1/\gamma} \;; \tag{2-8}$$

If so, the equations (2-3) and (2-4) can be reduced by elimination to

$$\frac{\partial^2 v}{\partial r^2} - \left\{\frac{1}{w}\frac{\partial w}{\partial r}\right\}\frac{\partial v}{\partial r} = \frac{w}{r^2}\left\{\sigma^2 + \frac{g}{\rho}\frac{\partial \rho}{\partial r} + \frac{g^2}{c^2}\frac{\rho v}{P^{2/\gamma}}\right\} , \qquad (2\text{-}9)$$

where we have abbreviated

$$w = \left\{\frac{j(j+1)}{\sigma^2} - \frac{r^2}{c^2}\right\}\frac{P^{2/\gamma}}{\rho} . \qquad (2\text{-}10)$$

The boundary conditions consistent with (2-6) and (2-7) are

$$v(0) = v(r_1) = 0 . \qquad (2\text{-}11)$$

Any further study of the properties of appropriate solutions of the equations (2-3)-(2-4) or (2-9) is possible only for configurations of particular equilibrium structure. Extensive numerical integrations of the polytropic family of models* have revealed that, for intermediate degrees of central condensation (say $\rho_c/\rho_m < 60$, corresponding to a polytropic index $n < 3.1$). A mode of oscillation is found, for any j, such that δr and $-\delta\rho$ are of the same algebraic sign throughout the interior. In addition to this fundamental oscillation, a discrete set of "overtone" oscillations are possible with periods both shorter and longer than that of the fundamental mode; and the quasi Sturm-Liouville character of the problem represented by equations (2-10)-(2-11) lends itself to a conjecture that these equations may admit of an infinite number of solutions representing non-radial oscillations with periods which can be both indefinitely long or short.

Moreover, a recent numerical investigation of the oscillatory properties of polytropic gas spheres of index n by Owen** led to a discovery of the fact that, for (approximately) $n > 3$, such spheres are no longer in a position to oscillate non-radially in the fundamental mode; and with increasing degree of central condensation, and increasing number of the overtones adjacent to the fundamental mode disappear from the discrete characteristic spectrum of free periods—until, for $n = 5$ (Roche model), the corresponding configuration loses completely the ability to oscillate non-radially in any free period at all. For very high degrees of central condensation (characteristic of, say, the index $4 < n < 5$), the discrete frequency spectrum of free periods consists essentially of very high modes of pressure oscillations (whose periods are very short), and of correspondingly high modes of gravitational oscillations (whose periods are again very long). The density of this

* Cf. T.G. Cowling, Mon. Not. Roy. Astr. Soc., 101, 367, 1941; Z. Kopal, Astroph. Journ., 109, 509, 1949; J. W. Owen, Mon. Not. Roy. Astr. Soc., 117, 384, 1947.

** J. W. Owen, Mon. Not. Roy. Astr. Soc., 117, 384, 1947.

frequency spectrum at either extreme makes it, moreover, very probable that the periods of some of its members may come indeed very close to the period of the binary orbit (as given by equation 0-4) and thus to resonate with the forced oscillations produced by orbital eccentricity. On the other hand, the very high modes of oscillation for which resonance becomes possible are characterized by so many nodes between the center and the surface that their damping (due to viscosity) is likely to be severe—thus restricting the amplitude which such oscillations may eventually attain. As a result, it seems impossible at present to predict the height of the partial tides to which a close coincidence of the orbital period with one of the permissible free oscillations can give rise. The mere possibility, however, that resonance can occur underlines the need of a dynamical theory of stellar tides—paralleling the equilibrium theory outlined in this volume—which is so far very largely lacking, and whose development represents an important desideratum of the theory of close binary system.

In conclusion of the present section, we wish to settle one more problem arising from the subject matter already discussed, to which the answer can be obtain with the means readily on hand: namely, under which conditions can non-radial oscillations of fluid globes become homologous? In order to answer this question, let us return to equation (2-8) and note that the ratio $\delta r/r$ represents a function which, in the case of forced oscillations, we used to denote by f . Let us, therefore, revert in (2-9) from v to f and, moreover, rewrite that equation in terms of the logarithmic derivative

$$\frac{r}{f}\frac{\partial f}{\partial r} = \eta \, . \tag{2-12}$$

The result reveals that, for free oscillations,

$$r\frac{\partial \eta}{\partial r} + (\eta+2)(\eta+3) - x\left\{r\frac{\partial x}{\partial r} - x + 2(\eta+3) - 1\right\}$$
$$- \frac{r}{w}\frac{\partial w}{\partial r}\{3+\eta-x\} = \left\{\frac{j(j+1)}{\sigma^2} - \frac{r^2}{c^2}\right\}\left\{\sigma^2 + \frac{g}{\rho}\frac{\partial \rho}{\partial r} + \frac{g^2}{c^2}\right\} , \tag{2-13}$$

where we have abbreviated

$$x = \frac{gr}{c^2} \, . \tag{2-14}$$

On the other hand, the radial displacements produced by forced oscillations of compressible fluids are known from Chapter II to obey the Radau equation

$$r\frac{\partial \eta}{\partial r} + 6D(\eta+1) + \eta(\eta-1) = j(j+1) , \tag{2-15}$$

where

$$D = \frac{\rho}{\bar{\rho}} = 1 + \frac{r}{3}\frac{\partial \log \bar{\rho}}{\partial r} \tag{2-16}$$

in accordance with (1-40) and (4-29) of Chapter II. Now if the free and forced non-radial oscillations are to be homologous, the foregoing equations (2-13) and (2-15) governing these respective displacements should become identical; and this will be the case if

$$6D = 6 - 2x - \frac{r}{w}\frac{\partial w}{\partial r} \tag{2-17}$$

and

$$r\frac{\partial x}{\partial r} - (x-2)(x-3) - (x-3)\frac{r}{w}\frac{\partial w}{\partial r} = j(j+1) - 6D - \left\{\frac{j(j+1)}{\sigma^2} - \frac{r^2}{c^2}\right\}\left\{\sigma^2 + \frac{g}{\rho}\frac{\partial \rho}{\partial r} + \frac{g^2}{c^2}\right\} \tag{2-18}$$

or, by use of (2-17)

$$r\frac{\partial x}{\partial r} + (x-3)(x-4+6D) = j(j+1) - 6D - \left\{\frac{j(j+1)}{\sigma^2} - \frac{r^2}{c^2}\right\}\left\{\sigma^2 + \frac{g}{\rho}\frac{\partial \rho}{\partial r} + \frac{g^2}{c^2}\right\}. \tag{2-19}$$

A combination of (2-16) and (2-17) reveals that

$$\frac{r}{w}\frac{\partial w}{\partial r} = -2\frac{gr}{c^2} - 2r\frac{\partial \log \rho}{\partial r} \tag{2-20}$$

or, by (2-5),

$$\frac{\partial \log w}{\partial r} = \frac{2}{\gamma}\frac{\partial \log P}{\partial r} - 2\frac{\partial \log \bar{\rho}}{\partial r}, \tag{2-21}$$

which readily integrates into

$$w = C P^{2/\gamma} \bar{\rho}^{-2}, \tag{2-22}$$

where C is constant. Inserting this result in equation (2-10) and particularizing for $r = 0$ we see, moreover, that

$$C = \frac{j(j+1)}{\sigma^2} \rho_c . \tag{2-23}$$

Hence, the validity of (2-17) implies that

$$\frac{j(j+1)}{\sigma^2}\ 1 - \frac{\rho\,\rho_c}{\bar{\rho}^2} = \frac{r^2}{c^2} \qquad (2-24)$$

and, as a consequence, equation (2-19) can be rewritten as

$$r\frac{\partial x}{\partial r} + (x-3)(x-4) = j(j+1)\left\{1 - D\frac{\rho_c}{\bar{\rho}}\left[1 - g\frac{\partial}{\partial r}\log(P^{1/\gamma}/\rho)\right]\right\}. \qquad (2-25)$$

Now if, consistent with our initial assumption of high central condensation, $D \sim 0$, the foregoing equations (2-24) and (2-25) should simplify into

$$\frac{r^2}{c^2} = \frac{j(j+1)}{\sigma^2} \qquad (2-26)$$

and

$$r\frac{\partial x}{\partial r} + (x-3)(x-4) = j(j+1)\ , \qquad (2-27)$$

which integrates into

$$x = \frac{gr}{c^2} = j+4 \ \text{ or } \ -j+3\ . \qquad (2-28)$$

As, lastly, the square c^2 of the velocity of sound is known to be proportional to the absolute temperature T, equation (2-26) implies that

$$T \sim r^2 \qquad (2-29)$$

while (2-28) implies that

$$T \sim gr \qquad (2-30)$$

which, for high central condensation (i.e., when $g = Gm_1/r$) is tantamount to

$$T \sim r^{-1}\ . \qquad (2-31)$$

A glance at the equations (2-29) and (2-31) reveals that these conditions (implied in 2-17 and 2-18) are inconsistent; and that the former is, moreover, absurd. Hence, it follows that in no self-gravitating fluid configuration can homology exist between displacements produced by free and forced non-radial oscillations—whatever its internal structure may be.

VI

BIBLIOGRAPHICAL NOTES

II-1: The method underlying the discussion in this section and leading to the fundamental equation (1-32) is, in principle, contained in a book, by A. C. Clairaut, entitled Théorie de la Figure de la Terre, tirée des Principes de l'Hydrostatique (Paris 1743); but its general form (for any value of j) does not appear to have been explicitly stated until fifty years later by A. M. Legendre in his Recherches sur la Figure des Planètes (Mémoires de Mathématique par divers Savants for 1789, but not actually published in Paris till 1793). The fifth volume of Laplace's Mécanique Céleste (Paris 1825) contains a comprehensive summary of this early work.

Its more recent partial summaries can be found, e.g., in F. Tisserand, Traité de la Mécanique Céleste (Paris 1891), Tome II, Chapters 13-18; H. Poincaré, Leçons sur les Figures d Equilibre (Paris 1903), chapter 4; H. Jeffreys, The Earth (Cambridge 1924), chapter 13, L. Lichtenstein, Gleichgewichtsfiguren rotierender Flüssigkeiten (Berlin 1933); W. S. Jardetzky, Theories of Figures of Celestial Bodies (New York 1958); Z. Kopal, Close Binary Systems (New York and London 1959), chapter 2, etc.

The name of Clairaut is customarily associated with the integral equation (1-32) or its differential equivalent (1-38). The logarithmic transformation (1-37) leading to the first-order equation (1-40) was likewise known (for j = 2) to Clairaut; but as it became the central point of Radau's investigations in C.R.Acad. Paris, 100, 972, 1885, or Bull. Astr., 2 , 157, 1885, it seems eminently appropriate to associate (1-40) with his name.

II-2: The general analysis of the nature of the solutions of Radau's equation, as given in this section, represents a generalization of previous discussions of this subject by H. Poincaré (Leçons sur les Figures d'Equilibre, Paris 1903, pp. 69-81) and A. Véronnet (Journ. de Math. (6), 8, 331, 1912). Both Poincaré and Véronnet limited their attention to the case of j = 2 only. The inequality (2-5) was, for j = 2 , proved previously by O. Callandreau (Bull. Astr., 5, 474, 1888) and A. Véronnet (op. cit.). The monotonically increasing nature of the function $\eta_2(a)$ under conditions (2-18) was first established by Callandreau in

C. R. Acad. Paris, 100, 1024, 1885.

The inequalities (2-27) or (2-28) were first proved in this form by Z. Kopal (Proc. U.S. Nat. Acad. Sci., 27, 359, 1941), while the more restricted form (2-29) was, of course, known long before: for $j = 2$ it was already implicit in Clairaut's work (op. cit.), although its rigorous proof was not supplied until the days of Poincaré.

The transformation (2-31) leading to (2-33) was used by Legendre and Airy.

With regard to the closed solutions of Clairaut-Radau equations for particular distributions of density in the interior, the density law (2-35) leading to a solution of the form (2-41) was considered already by Clairaut in his Théorie de la Figure de la Terre; while the hypothesis (2-37) underlying a density distribution (2-39) was introduced in Legendre's Recherches sur la Figure des Planètes, and Laplace discussed it in the fifth volume of his Mécanique Céleste. The present form (2-42) of its solution in terms of the Bessel functions of half-integral orders is, however, due to Kopal (Mon. Not. Roy. Astr. Soc., 99, 266, 1939).

The density law (2-48) and the solutions (2-57)-(2-58) in terms of the Jacobi polynomials based upon it represents the writer's generalization of particular cases considered previously by E. Roche (Mem. de l'Acad. des Sci. de Montpellier, 1848) and R. Lipschitz (Journ. de Crelle, 62, 1, 1863) for $k = \mu = 1$ and $j = \lambda = 2$. F. Tisserand (C. R. Acad. Paris, 99, 579, 1884) and M. Levy (C. R. Acad. Paris, 106, 1270, 1314, 1375, 1888) subsequently considered λ, μ as arbitrary constants, but retained the particular values of $j = 2$ and $k = 1$.

II-3: The method expounded in this section goes largely back to A. A. Liapounoff, Mem. de l'Acad. des Sci. de St. Pétersbourg, (8) 15, No. 10, 1904.

II-4: The iterative process outlined in the first part of this section is again Liapounoff's (op. cit.); while the formulation and solution of the boundary-value problem (4-16)-(4-18) resulting in the evaluation of the constants Δ_j by the quadrature formula (4-29) is due to Kopal (Mon. Not. Roy. Astr. Soc., 113, 769, 1953).

III. The extension of Clairaut's theory to second-order terms, as given in this chapter, has not previously been published except in the form of Technical Summary Reports of the Mathematics Research Center, U. S. Army, University of Wisconsin, No. 23 (March 1958) and No. 70 (January 1959), by the present writer. The text of this chapter constitutes an expanded version of these reports.

III-5: The only previous efforts to deal with the second-order terms due to axial rotation of self-gravitating fluids (much less complete or explicit than their present version) were made by O. Callandreau (Ann. de l'Observ. de Paris, 19 E, 1889), G. H. Darwin (Mon. Nat. Roy. Astr. Soc., 60, 82, 1900; Scientific Papers, Cambr. Univ. Press 1910, vol. 3, pp. 78 ff), A. Véronnet (Journ. de Math., (6) 8, 331, 1912);

or, more recently, by L. Evrard (Ann. d'Astroph., 14, 17, 1951), H. Jeffreys (Mon. Not. Roy. Astr. Soc., 113, 97, 1953); or W. C. de Marcus (Astron. Journ., 63, 2, 1958).

III-6: The closed solution (6-14) for the ellipticity of a rotating homogeneous spheroid was given first by C. Maclaurin in his Treatise of Fluxions, Edinburgh 1742.

The first formulation of the Roche model was given by its author in the Mémoires de l'Acad. des Sci. de Montpellier, 1, 243, 333; 2, 21, 1849-51. The results needed for comparison in the present section—and, in particular, equation (6-20)—have been taken from Chapter 3 of Kopal's Close Binary Systems (London and New York, 1959).

III-7 and 8: The results contained in these sections are mostly new.

IV. The content of this chapter is new, and has not previously been published by the writer except, partly, as a Technical Summary Report of Mathematics Research Center, U. S. Army, University of Wisconsin, No. 52 (October 1958).

V-1: Investigations of free non-radial oscillations of self-gravitating fluids go back to R. Emden, Gaskugeln, Leipzig 1907 (p. 448 ff), and S. Rosseland (Publ. Oslo Univ. Obs., No. 2, 1932). Its rigorous formulation for small adiabatic changes was given by Ch. Pekeris (Astroph. Journ., 88, 189, 1938), P. Ledoux (Proc. 3ème Congrès Nat. des Sci., Bruxelles, 2, 133, 1950), E. Sauvenier-Goffin (Bull. Soc. Roy. Sci. Liège, 20, 20, 1951), and others. For a comprehensive summary of much of this work cf. P. Ledoux, Handbuch der Physik, 51 (Astrophysik II), Berlin 1958, pp. 509-538.

V-2: The formulation of the problem of non-radial oscillation neglecting the disturbances δW in the gravitational potential has been initiated by T. G. Cowling (Mon. Not. Roy. Astr. Soc., 101, 367, 1941) and followed up by Z. Kopal (Astroph. Journ., 109, 509, 1949) and J. W. Owen (Mon. Not. Roy. Astr. Soc., 117, 384, 1957). All numerical work available on non-radial oscillations for the polytropic family of models is due to these three authors.

The proof that a homogeneous compressible configuration cannot oscillate non-radially was given first by Ch. Pekeris (Astroph. Journ., 88, 189, 1938); and the impossibility of non-radial oscillations of the mass-point (Roche) model was proved by J. Owen (Mon. Not. Roy. Astr. Soc., 117, 384, 1957). The proof as given in this section, of the fact that free and forced non-radial oscillations cannot be homologous, is new.

INDEX